AQA KS3

Science 2

Know and apply

PRACTICE BOOK

Cliff Curtis
Deborah Lowe
John Mynett

HODDER
EDUCATION
AN HACHETTE UK COMPANY

Hachette UK's policy is to use papers that are natural, renewable and recyclable products and made from wood grown in sustainable forests. The logging and manufacturing processes are expected to conform to the environmental regulations of the country of origin.

Orders: please contact Bookpoint Ltd, 130 Park Drive, Milton Park, Abingdon, Oxon OX14 4SE. Telephone: (44) 01235 827720. Fax: (44) 01235 400454. Email education@bookpoint.co.uk Lines are open from 9 a.m. to 5 p.m., Monday to Saturday, with a 24-hour message answering service. You can also order through our website: www.hoddereducation.co.uk

First published in 2018 by
Hodder Education,
An Hachette UK Company
Carmelite House
50 Victoria Embankment
London EC4Y 0DZ

www.hoddereducation.co.uk

Impression number 10 9 8 7 6 5 4 3 2 1

Year 2022 2021 2020 2019 2018

Cover photo © PCN Photography / Alamy Stock Photo

Typeset in 11/14 pt Vectora LT Std 45 Light by Integra Software Services Pvt. Ltd., Pondicherry, India

Printed in India

A catalogue record for this title is available from the British Library.

ISBN: 9781510402485

Contents

Find the answers at www.hoddereducation.co.uk/AQAKS3Science

1 Contact forces

» Combining forces

Worked example

The car below is initially stationary. The following forces are then applied.

50N   150N

a) Calculate the resultant force on the object.
b) Is the car in equilibrium?
c) What will happen to the motion of this object?

a) As the forces are in opposite directions, the resultant force is equal to the largest force minus the smallest force. Therefore, resultant force = 150 − 50 = 100 N to the right.

b) The car is not in equilibrium, because the resultant force is not zero.

c) The object will start to move to the right.

Know

1 What three effects can applying a force to an object have?

2 What are forces measured in?

3 What does the term 'resultant force' mean?

4 What is the resultant force of an object in equilibrium?

5 What will happen to an object in equilibrium if it is:

   a) stationary

   b) travelling at a steady speed?

Apply

1 Look at the diagrams below.

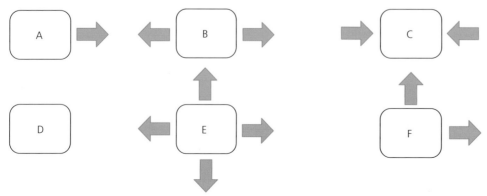

A   B   C

D   E   F

a) Which of the objects are in equilibrium?

b) If all of the objects were stationary to begin with, what would happen to the motion of each object when these forces were applied?

c) If all of the objects were travelling to the right at a steady speed to begin with, what would happen to the motion of each of object when these forces were applied?

2   Calculate the resultant force on each of the objects below.

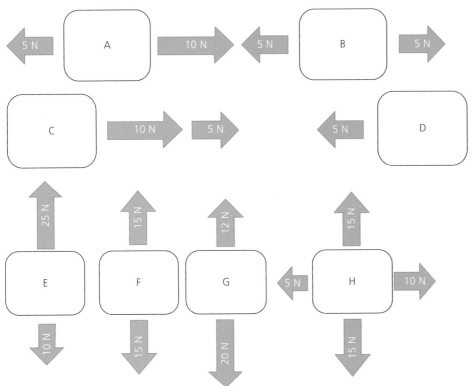

» Force diagrams

Worked example

Draw the forces acting on a bike as it travels at a steady speed. The weight of the bike (and cyclist) is 1000 N. The frictional forces (from the road and drag) working against the cyclist equal 500 N.

The question tells us about two forces. Weight acts downwards, and is twice as large as the frictional forces, which are against the cyclist.

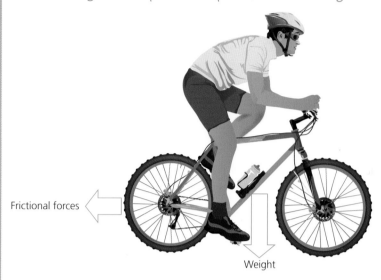

Frictional forces

Weight

If an object is travelling at a steady speed, it must be in equilibrium. Therefore, there must be a force that is an equal size to weight but acting upwards, and a force that is equal to the frictional forces but acting forwards.

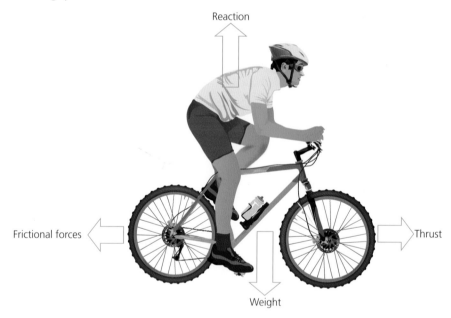

Reaction

Frictional forces

Thrust

Weight

Know

1 What three things does a force arrow tell us about a force, and how?

2 Add in the forces that must be present for the following objects to be in equilibrium.

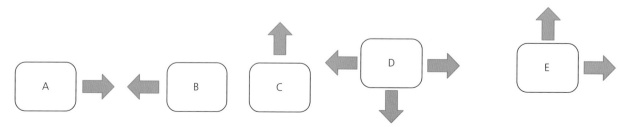

Apply

1 Draw and label the forces on the following objects.

   a) A book resting on a table.

   b) A car travelling at a steady speed.

   c) A skydiver speeding up as she falls to Earth.

   d) A rubber duck floating in a bath.

   e) A car decelerating (slowing down).

2 Draw force diagrams for the following situations, calculate the resultant force and describe what would happen to the motion of each object.

   a) A car with an engine force forwards of 300 N and a drag force backwards of 500 N.

   b) An anchor on the seabed with a weight of 200 N and a reaction force that balances this.

   c) A rocket with a thrust force of 1000 N and a weight of 800 N.

   d) A boat with a weight of 10 000 N and an upthrust force of 10 000 N.

» Effects of forces on shape

Worked example

A spring is originally 15 cm long. When two 100 g masses are added to the end of it, its length increases to 25 cm.

a) What is the force applied to the spring in this situation?
b) What is the extension of the spring?
c) How long would the spring be if a third 100 g mass was added?

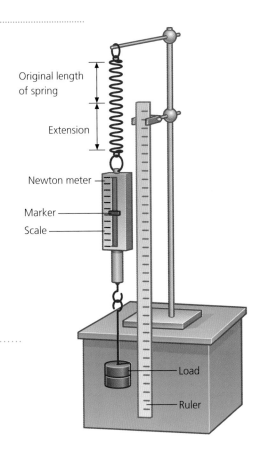

a) The force is caused by the weight of the masses:

   weight = mass × gravitational field strength = 0.2 kg × 10 = 2 N

b) Extension is how much the length has increased by:

   extension = 25 cm – 15 cm = 10 cm

c) Two masses cause a 10 cm extension, so one mass would cause half of this, 5 cm. Therefore the spring would have a length of 25 cm + 5 cm = 30 cm.

Know

1 When does deformation occur?

2 What is the difference between tension and compression?

3 What is the difference between the independent and the dependent variable in an investigation?

4 Give some examples of when forces can deform objects.

Apply

1 When a force (or load) is applied to a spring, it stretches. If we increase that load, the extension of the spring increases too. We can sketch a graph of this experiment as follows:

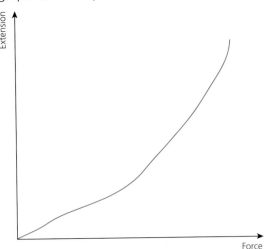

a) Which is the independent variable in the experiment and which is the dependent variable? Why?

b) How does the graph show that the force applied is directly proportional to the extension (at least to start with)?

c) Where is the elastic limit of the spring shown on the graph?

d) What will happen to the spring if it is stretched past its elastic limit?

e) How would the graph look different for a spring with a higher elastic limit?

f) How would the graph look different for a more stretchy spring?

2 Pressure

Floating and sinking

Worked example

A small rowing boat displaces 800 N of water when it is put into a lake.
a) What must the weight of the rowing boat be, if it is floating?
b) What is the mass of the boat?

a) If the boat is floating, the weight of water displaced must equal the weight of the boat. Therefore, the boat must weigh 800 N.

b) The mass of the boat can be calculated using the equation:

weight = mass × gravitational field strength

Therefore, rearranging the equation in terms of mass:

$$mass = \frac{weight}{gravitational\ field\ strength}$$

$$mass = \frac{800\,N}{10\,N/kg} = 80\,kg$$

Know

What is upthrust?

What do we mean when we say that water is displaced when an object is put in it?

Copy and complete the diagrams below by adding in an arrow showing the direction and size of the upthrust force for each situation.

Note: the anchor is sinking.

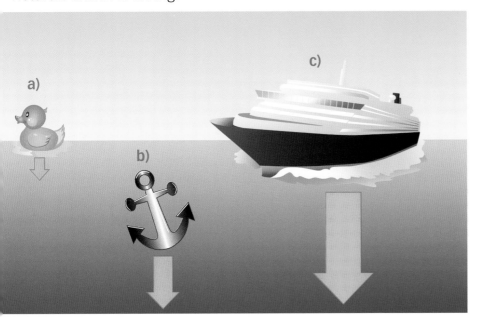

4 What equation relates mass and weight?

5 Copy and complete the sentences below.

   a) We can work out whether an object will float or sink by comparing the _____ of the object with the _____ of the water it _____.

   b) If the weight of the object is equal to weight of water it displaces, it will _____.

   c) If the weight of water is less than the weight of the object, it will _____.

Apply

1 Copy and complete the table below. The first row has been completed for you.

Mass of object	Weight of object	Weight of water the object must displace if it is to float
1 kg	10 N	10 N
500 g	5 N	
0.2 kg		
15 kg		150 N
	200 N	
		8 N
300 g		
	0.5 N	

2 For each of the objects below, draw a force diagram for the situation and decide whether the object will float or sink. Then calculate the mass of each object.

   a) A cork weighs 0.1 N and displaces 0.1 N of water.

   b) A pineapple weighs 5 N and displaces 3 N of water.

3 A 1000 kg boat must displace what weight of water if it is to float?

» Forces on a surface

Worked example

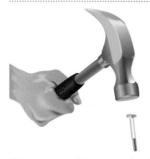

A hammer hits a nail with a force of 300 N. The head of the nail has a surface area of 0.0005 m², whilst the sharp end has a surface area of 0.00002 m². Calculate the difference in stress between the two ends of the nail.

To answer this question, we must use the equation:

$$\text{stress} = \frac{\text{force}}{\text{area}}$$

The force is the same in both situations, but the area is not.

For the head of the nail:

$$\text{stress} = \frac{\text{force}}{\text{area}} = \frac{300\,\text{N}}{0.0005\,\text{m}^2} = 600\,000\,\text{N/m}^2$$

For the end of the nail:

$$\text{stress} = \frac{\text{force}}{\text{area}} = \frac{300\,\text{N}}{0.00002\,\text{m}^2} = 15\,000\,000\,\text{N/m}^2$$

The difference in stress is:

$$15\,000\,000\,\text{N/m}^2 - 600\,000\,\text{N/m}^2 = 14\,400\,000\,\text{N/m}^2$$

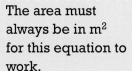

> **Hint**
>
> The area must always be in m² for this equation to work.

Know

1 What is stress?

2 What is the equation for stress?

3 What unit is stress measured in?

4 What unit must the area always be in for the equation to work?

5 What is the area of the following situations, in m²?

   a) A square with sides that are each 2m long.

   b) A rectangle with sides that are 3m and 5m long.

   c) A triangle of base 4m and height 2m.

   d) A square with sides that are each 50cm long.

   e) A rectangle with sides that are 35mm and 15mm long.

6 When you stand on the floor, you exert a stress on it. How could you:

   a) increase this stress

   b) decrease this stress?

7 Put the following shoes in order of how much stress they would exert on the floor if you were wearing them, from the least stress to the most.

   A wellington boots

   B stiletto heels

   C snow shoes

8 State two examples of high-stress situations and two examples of low-stress situations.

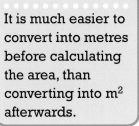

> **Hint**
>
> It is much easier to convert into metres before calculating the area, than converting into m² afterwards.

> **Hint**
>
> The area of a square or rectangle is equal to base × height. The area of a triangle is equal to ½ × base × height.

Apply

1 Copy and complete the table below. The first row has been done for you.

Force (N)	Area (m²)	Stress (N/m²)
500	5	100
250	50	
100	2	
	3	15
	5	20
14		2
5		10
3	0.2	
2000	0.01	
	0.005	20 000
30 000		300 000

2 A drawing pin has a head that is approximately 0.005 m² and an end that is approximately 0.0002 m². You push it into a wall with a force of 50 N. What stress does the pin exert on

   a) your thumb

   b) the wall?

3 A wooden cube has sides that are each 4 cm long and has a mass of 200 g.

   a) Convert 4 cm into metres.

   b) Calculate the area of one side of a block.

   c) Convert 200 g into kilograms.

   d) Determine the weight of the block.

   e) Calculate the stress that one block will exert on the ground.

   f) Calculate the stress that four blocks, laid horizontally, will exert on the ground.

   g) Calculate the stress that four blocks, stacked vertically, will exert on the ground.

4 You are standing on a frozen pond and the ice is about to crack due to the stress you are exerting on it. How could you reduce the chance of falling into the water? Explain why.

» Pressure in a fluid

Worked example

A diver has a surface area of $0.4\,m^2$. Whey they are $2\,m$ below sea level, there is $800\,kg$ of water above them. What pressure do they experience due to this?

Using the equation:

$$pressure = \frac{force}{area}$$

The force is the weight of the water above the diver. So

$$weight = mass \times g = 800 \times 10 = 8000\,N$$

then

$$pressure = \frac{force}{area} = \frac{8000}{0.4} = 20\,000\,Pa$$

Know

1 What is pressure?

2 What is the equation for pressure?

3 What three units can be used for pressure?

4 How many pascals are in a kilopascal?

5 What do we mean by 'atmospheric pressure'?

6 How many pascals are in 1 atmosphere of pressure?

7 Put these in order of how much pressure you would feel from the environment if you were there, from highest to lowest.

   A at sea level

   B at the top of Mount Everest

   C at the bottom of the Atlantic Ocean

   D at the top of the Empire State Building

   E at the bottom of a swimming pool

Apply

1 Compare the similarities and differences between stress and pressure.

2 Describe how fluids can cause pressure.

3 Copy and complete the table below. The first row has been done for you.

Force (N)	Area (m²)	Pressure (Pa)
200	5	40
1000	50	
440	8	
	6	36
	20	18
25		2
3		10
60	0.3	
3500	0.0002	
	0.01	55 000
480 000		16

4 The area of your head and shoulders is approximately 0.1 m². If atmospheric pressure is 100 kPa at sea level, what is the weight of the air molecules above you?

5 Water pressure increases by about 1 atmosphere for every 10 m that you travel beneath the water's surface. What would the water pressure on you be, in atmospheres and kPa at:

a) 10 m below the surface

b) 25 m below the surface

c) 100 m below the surface (a recommended limit for divers)

6 Explain why air pressure is lower at the top of a mountain compared with at sea level.

3 Electromagnets

» Stronger electromagnets

Worked example

Some students make two electromagnets.
- Electromagnet A is made of 10 coils of wire and is connected to two 1.5V cells.
- Electromagnet B is made of 20 coils of wire and is connected to one 1.5V cell.

Which electromagnet would have the strongest magnetic field surrounding it?

This is a bit of a trick question! The strength of an electromagnet relies mainly on two factors – the number of coils in it and the size of the current passing through it, which depends on the voltage applied to the circuit. Electromagnet A has half the number of coils of electromagnet B so would have a smaller magnetic field around it if they were both carrying the same current. However, electromagnet A is connected to twice the number of cells, and so will have twice the current passing through. This, in effect, 'cancels out' the effect of only having half the number of coils. Therefore, electromagnets A and B would both have the same strength magnetic field around them.

Know

1. What happens when you place a compass near an electric circuit?

2. What is caused when charges move through a conductor?

3. What is electromagnetism?

4. What can happen when the following objects are placed near an electromagnet?

   a) another electromagnet

   b) a permanent magnet

   c) a magnetic material

   d) a non-magnetic material

5. Do electromagnets follow the same rules as permanent magnets when it comes to attraction and repulsion?

6. 'Only iron, nickel and cobalt can be made into an electromagnet.' Is this statement correct?

7. When are electromagnets used instead of permanent magnets?

8. How do you switch an electromagnet on or off?

9 How can you increase or decrease the current in an electric circuit?

10 What dangers do the following pose?

   a) high voltage

   b) high current

11 What is a solenoid? Draw a diagram to help you explain.

12 State three ways to increase the strength of an electromagnet.

Apply

1 Compare an electromagnet with a permanent magnet.

2 Wrapping a wire around an iron nail can make a simple electromagnet.

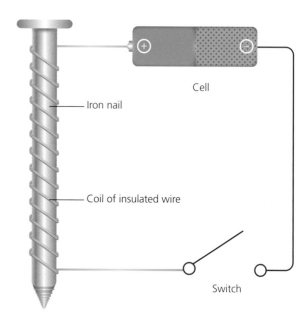

Cell

Iron nail

Coil of insulated wire

Switch

   What would happen to the magnetic field around the electromagnet in the circuit shown above if:

   a) more coils were added to the wire

   b) the cell was turned around

   c) another cell was added

   d) some coils were taken away

   e) the switch was opened

   f) the iron nail was taken away, leaving the coiled wire behind?

3 Explain why a solenoid causes a stronger magnetic field than a piece of straight wire.

4 Sketch the fields around the following solenoids, assuming they carry the same size current in each case.

   a)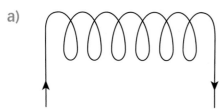

   b)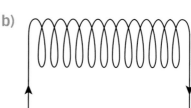

» Using electromagnets

Worked example

A student needs to separate a mixture of sand and iron filings into two piles. Explain the advantages of using an electromagnet to do this over a permanent magnet.

The student can use any type of magnet to separate the mixture; the magnetic iron filings will be attracted to the magnet, leaving the non-magnetic sand behind. The advantage comes in the second step; it will be very hard to take the iron filings off the permanent magnet, as they will always be attracted to it. Using an electromagnet would be better here, as when the power supply is switched off the electromagnet will stop being magnetic, causing the iron filings to fall off the magnet into a separate pile.

Know

State two advantages of electromagnets over permanent magnets.

Electromagnets are used in recycling plants to sort out rubbish. Which of the following objects would the electromagnet pick up?

A plastic cups   E aluminium cans

B tinfoil trays   F old fridge

C newspapers   G wooden table

D steel cans

State three other uses of electromagnets in everyday life.

Apply

Loudspeakers use permanent and electromagnets to work. Put the following sentences in the correct order to explain how.

A The cone (containing the electromagnet) moves towards the permanent magnet.

B This causes a magnetic field around the solenoid.

C This causes a force between the electromagnet and the permanent magnet.

D A current runs through the electromagnet.

Explain how the force between the electromagnet and the permanent magnet in a loud speaker can be:

a) increased and decreased in strength

b) switched between attraction and repulsion.

4 Magnetism

» Magnetism and navigation

Worked example

The north pole of a magnet is held near three sealed boxes containing hidden objects – another magnet, an iron nail and a wooden block. A student experiments with the boxes and finds that:

* box A is attracted to the magnet
* box B is not attracted to the magnet
* box C is repulsed from the magnet.

Which object is in which box?

Magnets can attract either other magnets or magnetic materials, so box A must contain either the other magnet or the iron nail (as iron is a magnetic material). However, we cannot yet tell which one it is. Box B is unaffected by the magnet, so must contain the non-magnetic material – the wooden block.

The magnet repels box C. Only another magnet can be repelled by a magnet, so box C must contain the second magnet. That means that box A must contain the iron nail.

Know

1 What is a permanent magnet?

2 Which three metals are magnetic?

3 What is a magnetic field?

4 What does the strength of a magnetic field depend on?

5 Where is the magnetic force due to a magnet strongest – near the magnet or far away?

6 Copy and complete the rules below:

   a) Opposite poles _____.

   b) Like poles _____.

   c) A magnet will _____ a magnetic material.

7 Sort the following into magnetic and non-magnetic objects:

   A copper wire
   B nails and screws
   C plastic comb
   D fridge door
   E paper clips
   F wooden block
   G screwdriver
   H pound coin

8 State two ways in which magnetism can be used to help with navigation.

Apply

1 Why is magnetism an example of a non-contact force?

2 What is the difference between an attractive and a repulsive force?

3 What would happen in the following situations? Will they attract, repulse or do nothing?

» Magnetic fields

Worked example

Below is a diagram of the Earth's magnetic field.

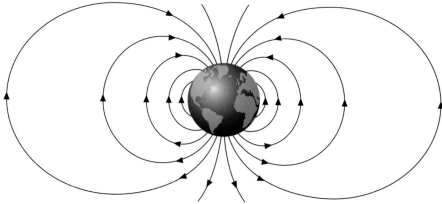

a) Label the magnetic north and south poles.

b) Indicate where on the Earth its magnetic field is weakest and explain your decision.

a) The arrows of the magnetic field lines always point from the north pole to the south pole. Therefore, the magnetic south pole is at the top of the Earth (the geographic north pole) and the magnetic north pole is at the bottom (the geographic south pole).

b) The strength of the field is shown by how close or far apart the field lines are. The lines are closes together at the poles and furthest apart at the sides, over the Equator. Therefore, the field is weakest at the Equator.

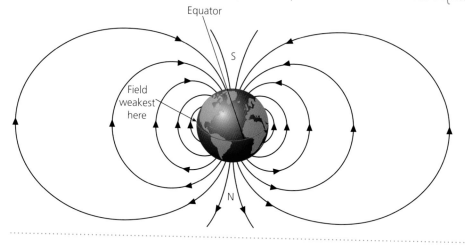

Know

1 What happens when you place a compass near a magnet?

2 Copy and complete the sentences below:

   a) The arrows on magnetic field lines point from the _____ pole to the _____ pole.

   b) The closer together the field lines are, the _____ the magnetic field is.

3 Which materials can block a magnetic field?

4 How can a magnetic material be made into a permanent magnet?

Apply

1 Describe what is being shown in the diagram below.

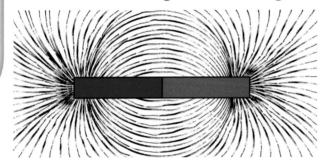

2 Describe how a plotting compass can be used to draw the magnetic field of a magnet.

3 Copy the diagrams below and add in arrows at each numbered position, to show which way the compasses would point.

   a)

   b)

4 Sketch the magnetic field around a bar magnet and label which parts of the field are the strongest.

5 Sketch the magnetic field around the Earth and compare it with the field around a bar magnet.

6 Explain why steel lasts longer as a permanent magnet than iron.

5 Work

» Pushing and pulling

Worked example

Charlie walks up two different flights of stairs. Both are 5 m tall, but flight A has 20 shallow steps whilst flight B has 10 steeper steps.

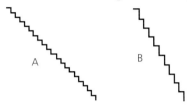

a) What force is he doing work against?
b) Which flight of stairs requires more work to be done to climb it?
c) How much more work would need to be done to climb flight A if it was twice as tall?

a) Charlie is doing work against the force of gravity – he is working against his own weight.
b) This is a bit of a trick question. Although flight A will require Charlie to walk a longer distance overall, both flights of stairs require Charlie to move a vertical distance of 5 m. Work done depends on the distance travelled in the direction of the force. As the force here is gravity, which acts vertically, we only need to think about how far Charlie has travelled vertically. As both flights have a vertical distance of 5 m, they both require Charlie to do the same amount of work to climb them – it does not matter how many steps there are.
c) Work done depends on the force and the distance travelled in the direction of the force. Doubling the height here doubles the distance, and so doubles the amount of work done when climbing it.

Know

1 What can forces do to the motion of an object?

2 What does work mean in physics?

3 What is work measured in?

4 What else is measured in this unit?

5 What direction will an object move in when work is done?

6 How can you increase the amount of work done on an object?

7 When does deformation occur?

8 Give an example of a situation where work is done on an object to deform it.

Apply

1 State three situations where:

   a) you do work

   b) work is done on you.

2 You are pushing a pram along a road.

   a) What force are you doing work against?

   b) What direction is this force in?

   c) What is the energy transfer in this situation?

3 Lifting an apple 1 m vertically requires approximately 1 J of work.

   a) What force is work being done against?

   b) What is the energy transfer in this situation?

   c) How much work would be done if two apples were lifted instead?

   d) How much work would be done if the single apple was lifted 3 m?

   e) How much work would be done if four apples were lifted 2 m?

   f) How could you do 6 J of work with these apples?

4 Which of the following situations involve work being done? For each one, identify which force work is being done against.

   a) Walking up a flight of stairs.

   b) Holding an apple out at arm's length.

   c) Sliding down a slide.

   d) Sitting on a chair.

   e) Lifting a book.

   f) Squeezing a stress ball.

   g) Squeezing a brick.

» Simple machines

Worked example

Explain why it is easier to undo a tightened bolt using a long spanner rather than a short one.

A spanner is an example of a lever, which is a type of simple machine. When you undo a bolt, you are doing work, which follows the equation:

work = force applied × distance to the pivot

Here, the pivot would be around the bolt. Therefore, for a long spanner, the distance to the pivot would be larger so less force would be needed to do the same amount of work as the short spanner.

Know

1 What is a simple machine?

2 State three examples of simple machines.

3 How do wheels make work easier?

4 What is the difference between an input and output force?

5 What is a lever?

6 What is a fulcrum?

Apply

1 Compare distance and displacement.

2 Describe three situations in which you use a lever to help you do work.

6 Heating and cooling

» Temperature changes

Worked example

A cup of hot chocolate is left out on a table to cool. Its temperature is taken every 2 minutes and the following graph is produced.

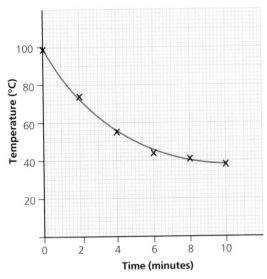

a) When did the hot chocolate have the largest store of thermal energy?
b) Describe the direction of energy transfer.
c) How long (approximately) did it take the hot chocolate to cool to 60°C?
d) How did the rate of energy transfer change over the 10 minutes? Explain your reasoning.
e) How would the graph look different if the hot chocolate were cooled in a fridge?

a) At the start of the experiment (0 minutes), when it had the highest temperature.
b) The energy transfers from the hot chocolate to its surroundings.
c) Just over 3 minutes (by reading off the graph).
d) The rate of energy transfer slows down, because the temperature decreases more slowly over time; there is a bigger difference in temperature between readings at the start compared with at the end.
e) If the hot chocolate were cooled in a fridge, the energy would transfer away more quickly and the temperature would decrease more quickly. Therefore, the curve on the graph would be steeper.

Know

1 What is the temperature of an object, a measure of?

2 What is the thermal store of energy, a measure of?

3   Which will have the largest store of thermal energy, a hot object or a cold object?

4   Draw the arrangement of particles in a solid, liquid and gas.

5   What is a fluid?

6   Which of the following are fluids?

   A   solids

   B   liquids

   C   gases

7   Which of the following fluids would have the fastest-moving particles? Which would have the slowest?

   A   cold liquid

   B   hot liquid

   C   cold gas

   D   hot gas

8   How do the particles in a solid change their motion when the solid is heated up?

9   Describe how the motion of particles in a liquid would change as it cooled down.

10 Which way will the energy transfer in each of the following situations?

   a)   a frozen pizza put in an oven

   b)   hot soup put in a fridge

   c)   cold milk poured into a hot coffee

   d)   an ice cube put in your mouth

Apply

1   Look at the table below.

Object	Temperature (°C)
A	10
B	34
C	−5
D	26
E	0
F	−14

   a)   Which object has the biggest store of thermal energy?

   b)   Which object has the smallest store of thermal energy?

   c)   In which object will the particles be moving the most quickly? Why?

   d)   In which object will the particles be moving the least quickly? Why?

e) What would the temperature difference be between objects:

    i) A and B

    ii) D and E

    iii) C and F

    iv) A and C?

f) Which two objects would have the most energy flow between them if they were put in contact? Why?

g) Which two objects would have the least energy flow between them if they were put in contact? Why?

2 Putting an ice cube in a drink causes the liquid to cool down.

a) Why is this, in terms of energy transfers?

b) When will the drink stop cooling down?

» Conduction

Worked example

Most saucepans are made of metal, with handles made of either plastic or wood.

a) What process allows heat to travel from the hob to whatever is inside the pan?

b) Which of these materials are conductors and which are insulators?

c) Why are these properties important for the pan and its user?

a) Heat travels from the hob to whatever is inside the pan via conduction.

b) Metal is a conductor. Plastic and wood are insulators.

c) A conductor allows heat to travel through it easily. This is important for the pan so that the heat from the hob can travel to the contents of the pan and warm them up. An insulator does not allow heat to travel through it easily. This is important for the handle so that whoever is using the pan does not get burnt.

Know

1 What is conduction?

2 What is a thermal insulator?

3 What is a thermal conductor?

4 Give three examples of:

a) good thermal insulators

b) good thermal conductors.

5 Put the following in order (best to worst) of how good they are at

a) conducting and

b) insulating:

- copper

- air

- plastic

Apply

1 How can thermochromic film be used to measure temperature?

2 Which is most likely to be the best conductor: a solid, a liquid or a gas? Why?

3 Which is most likely to be the best insulator: a solid, a liquid or a gas? Why?

4 Why are metals generally the best thermal conductors?

5 Draw a diagram to show how conduction occurs in:

a) non-metals

b) metals.

» Convection

Worked example

Kettles boil water by setting up convection currents. Make a flow chart to explain how they work, using a diagram to help.

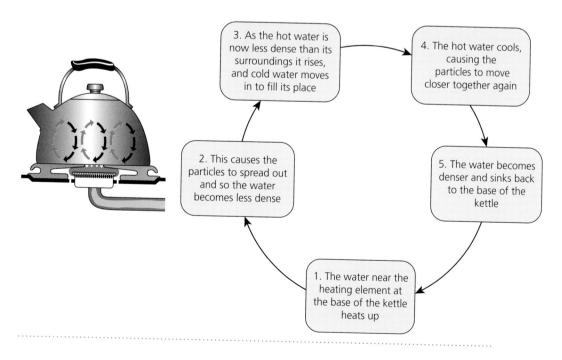

3. As the hot water is now less dense than its surroundings it rises, and cold water moves in to fill its place

4. The hot water cools, causing the particles to move closer together again

2. This causes the particles to spread out and so the water becomes less dense

5. The water becomes denser and sinks back to the base of the kettle

1. The water near the heating element at the base of the kettle heats up

Know

1 What is convection?

2 What happens to the density of a fluid when it is heated?

3 What is the equation for density?

4 Why do hot air balloons float in the air?

5 In a convection current, what happens to:

   a) a warm fluid

   b) a cold fluid?

6 Put these sentences in order, to describe how convection takes place when heating water in a pan.

   A The water rises.

   B The water at the base of the pan gets hotter.

   C As it moves away from the base, it cools down.

   D It becomes denser and sinks again.

   E This causes the water particles to spread out and the water becomes less dense.

Apply

1 A convection tube is a piece of equipment that demonstrates convection currents in the lab.

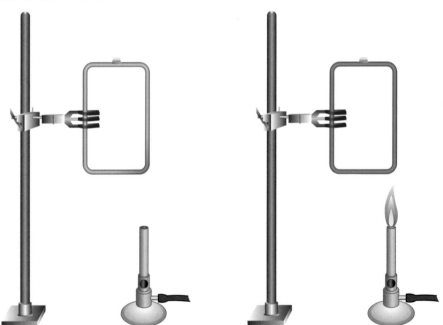

As shown in the diagram, a small amount of blue dye is put in one corner of the tube. A Bunsen burner is placed beneath this corner and turned on. The dye rises up and travels around the tube, colouring all of the water.

   a) Why does the dye rise up when the Bunsen burner is turned on?

   b) Why does it fall back down again when it reaches the opposite corner?

» Radiation

Worked example

Two children are playing on a sunny day. Annie is wearing a white t-shirt, whilst Peter is wearing a black one. Who will feel the warmest, and why?

Peter will feel warmer than Annie, because black is a better absorber of heat than white, and white is a better reflector of heat than black. Therefore, Peter's black t-shirt will absorb more of the sunlight's energy, whilst Annie's t-shirt will reflect more of it.

Know

1 What is radiation?

2 What is infrared radiation?

3 What emits infrared radiation?

4 Which of the following absorbs infrared radiation more:

   a) dark or light surfaces

   b) shiny or matte surfaces?

5 Give three examples of when heat is transferred by radiation.

Apply

1 How do we know that radiation can travel through a vacuum?

2 Why is it more comfortable to wear light colours on a hot day than dark ones? Explain using ideas about radiation.

3 Radiators are usually painted white, but it would be more sensible not to.

   a) What colour should they be painted to emit the most radiation possible?

   b) Why do you think this is not done?

7 Wave effects

» Sounds and explosions

Worked example

While filming an action movie, a film crew needs to set up an explosion.
a) What type of waves will this explosion cause to be emitted?
b) How would these waves be different if the explosion was bigger?
c) How might these waves be detected by the actors working nearby?
d) What safety procedures might the cast and crew follow to reduce their risk of harm?

a) An explosion would cause pressure waves, including sound waves. It would also cause light and infrared (heat) waves to be emitted.
b) The sound and pressure waves would have a bigger amplitude, as they would carry more energy. The explosion might also produce more light and heat waves.
c) The actors would be able to see the light waves and feel the infrared waves. They would be able to hear the sound waves and might be able to feel the other pressure waves on their body.
d) They need to be as far away as possible. This is because the energy from the explosion spreads out – the further away they are, the 'weaker' the waves will be.

Know

1 State three examples of waves.

2 What is a wave?

3 What do waves transfer?

4 State five keywords that can be used to describe waves.

5 State two things that absorption of a wave can cause.

6 Apart from absorption, what else can waves do when they encounter an obstacle?

7 What is a medium?

8 What is a pressure wave?

9 State some causes of pressure waves.

10 What does a microphone convert sound waves into?

11 What does a loudspeaker convert electrical signals into?

Apply

1 Describe how sound travels from a source to a detector through a medium.

2 How would the current produced by a loud sound in a microphone be different from that produced by a quiet sound?

3 Why is it hard to measure the wavelength of sound? Give two reasons.

4 How can the speed of sound be measured?

» Nearly visible

Worked example

Visible light is part of a family of waves called the electromagnetic spectrum. These waves have different wavelengths and frequencies, which cause them to have different properties. A diagram of this family is shown below.

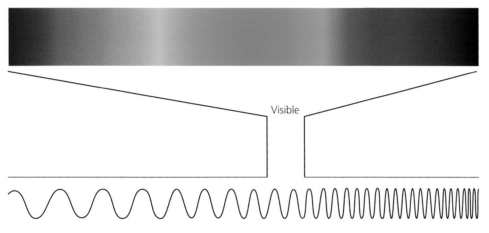

a) Label on the diagram where ultraviolet light and infrared radiation would be situated.
b) Which of these has the longest wavelength?
c) Which of these has the highest frequency?
d) Which of these can cause damage when living cells absorb it?
e) How can the other types cause damage to humans?

a) Ultraviolet light is light that is 'too violet' for humans to see, so it must go just past the violet end of the visible spectrum. Likewise, infrared radiation is light that is 'too red' for humans to see, and so must be situated just past the red end of the visible spectrum, like so:

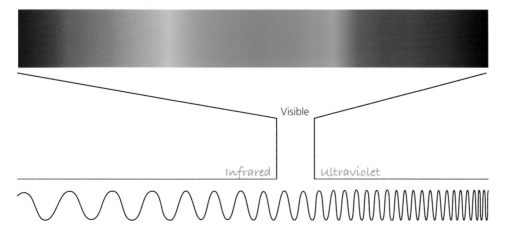

b) Infrared radiation
c) Ultraviolet light
d) Ultraviolet light
e) Infrared radiation causes burns – it is another word for heat. Visible light can damage eyes, if you look at a bright source for too long.

Know

1 State a difference between sound and light waves.

2 What is ultrasound?

3 What is infrasound?

4 What is ultraviolet light?

5 What is infrared radiation?

6 What types of radiation does the Sun emit?

Apply

1 When can ultraviolet waves cause damage to humans?

2 How can this damage be increased?

3 Compare the risks and benefits of ultraviolet light.

4 How can people reduce the risk of ultraviolet light, so that they can enjoy being in the sunshine?

5 Infra- and ultra- are prefixes that are used for both sound and light. What do you think these prefixes mean?

8 Wave properties

» Wave behaviour

Worked example

Frosted glass is used in bathroom windows, to allow light in without letting people see inside. Explain how light behaves when it hits a frosted glass window, and compare this with a normal window.

When light hits either normal or frosted glass most of it is transmitted and travels through to the other side. As it does this, it will probably refract (or bend) slightly as it passes from the air to the glass and then later from the glass to the air. A little bit of light may also be reflected – it may bounce off the window. This is why you can often see your reflection in a window.

The difference between frosted glass and normal glass is in the amount of light it absorbs. Normal glass will absorb too little light to measure. However, frosted glass will absorb much more light, and the energy that it carries is transferred into the glass, causing it to heat up slightly.

Know

1 What is reflection?

2 Can all waves be reflected?

3 What types of surface best reflect:

   a) light

   b) sound?

4 What is the difference between absorption and transmission?

5 What is refraction?

6 Give an example of a material that would:

   a) reflect light

   b) absorb light

   c) transmit light

   d) refract light?

Apply

1 If a surface is not a perfect reflector, what else could also happen to the wave?

2 Is the light in the following photographs being reflected, absorbed, transmitted, refracted or a combination of these?

a)   b)

c)   d)

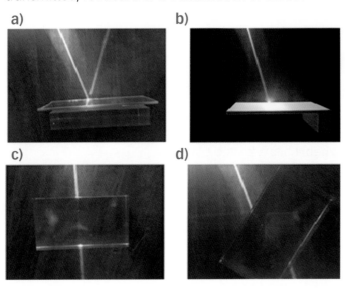

3 What would happen to light if it hit the following materials?

   a) air

   b) black card

   c) tin foil

   d) coloured glass

   e) water

4 Use ideas of absorption and reflection to explain why it is uncomfortable to wear black clothes on a sunny day.

» Numbers

Worked example

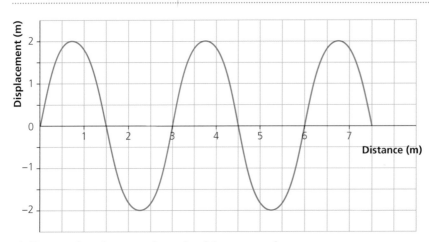

a) Determine the wavelength of the wave above.
b) Determine the amplitude of the wave above.
c) Add a second wave to the diagram, with half the amplitude of the first one.
d) Which of these waves would carry more energy? Why?

a) The wavelength of a wave is the distance between two adjacent identical places on the wave, for example between a peak and the next peak or a trough and the next trough. Here, that would be 3 m.

b) The amplitude is the distance between the midpoint of the wave (here, the x-, or distance axis) and the peak or trough of the wave. Here, that would be 2 m.

c) The amplitude of the new wave should be 1 m, but we need to keep the wavelength the same. Therefore the new wave would look like this:

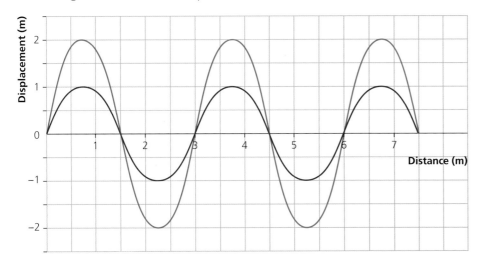

d) The original wave. The energy a wave carries is related to its amplitude and, because the first wave has double the amplitude of the one that we have added, it has more energy.

Know

1 Put these waves in order of speed, from fastest to slowest:

   A Sound in air

   B Light in a vacuum

   C Ripples in a pond

2 Draw a diagram of a wave and label the amplitude and wavelength.

3 Copy and complete the paragraph below using the following key words:

adjacent	distance	horizontal	energy	ruler
vertical	identical	maximum	peak	metres	trough

The wavelength of a wave is the _____ between repeating waves. It is measured on a diagram using a ruler and is the _____ distance between _____ points on two _____ waves (waves that are next to each other). The amplitude of a wave is the _____ amount of vibration of the wave, and is related to how much _____ the wave is carrying. It is also measured on a diagram using a _____ and is the _____ distance between the mid-point of the wave and either the top of the _____ or the bottom of the _____. Both the wavelength and amplitude of a wave are measured in _____.

Apply

1 Measure the amplitude and wavelength of each of the waves below.

a)

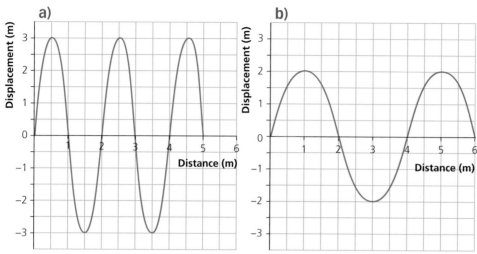

b)

c)

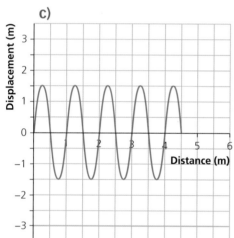

d)

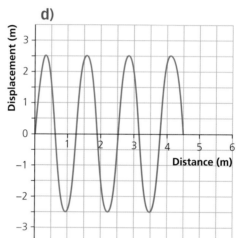

2 What's wrong with the following diagrams?

a)

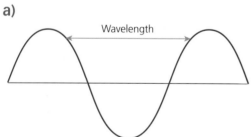

b)

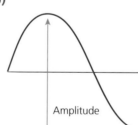

c)

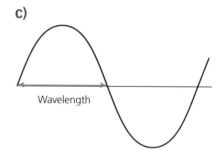

3 Copy and complete the table below. The first row has been done for you.

Wave speed	Distance	Time
4 m/s	8 m	2 s
	150 m	3 s
	40 m	10 s
	1.5 km	30 s
5 m/s	250 m	
3 m/s	9 m	
10 m/s	3 km	
15 m/s		2 s
2 m/s		1 minute
18 m/s		25 s
5 km/s	15 000 m	

4 A water wave travels 50 km in 20 seconds. What is its wave speed?

5 Sound travels at 340 m/s in air.

   a) How long would it take a noise to travel 1 km?

   b) How far would a noise travel in 2 minutes?

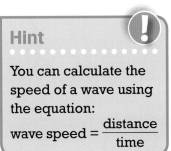

Hint

You can calculate the speed of a wave using the equation:

$$\text{wave speed} = \frac{\text{distance}}{\text{time}}$$

» Waves and time/ two waves at once

Worked example

A student counts 20 water waves in a ripple tank passing a point in 5 seconds.
a) What is the frequency of the water waves?
b) What is the period of the water waves?

a) Frequency is the number of waves that pass a point per second. If 20 water waves pass in 5 seconds, then $\frac{20}{5}$ = 4 waves must pass in 1 second. Therefore, the frequency of the water waves is 4 Hz.

b) Period is how long it takes for one complete wave to pass a point. If four waves pass a point per second, then it must take $\frac{1}{4}$ = 0.25 seconds for each wave to pass the point. Therefore, the period of the wave is 0.25 seconds.

Know

a) What is meant by the 'frequency' of a wave and what is it measured in?

b) What is meant by the 'period' of a wave and what is it measured in?

c) How are frequency and period related to each other?

Apply

1 A radio wave has a frequency of 3 000 000 Hz. What does this mean in simple terms?

2 A boy drops a pebble in pond, creating a ripple. 10 ripples are made in 2 seconds.

    a) What is the frequency of the ripples?

    b) What is the period of one ripple?

3 The musical note 'middle C' has a frequency of about 260 Hz.

    a) How long would it take for 1000 'middle C' sound waves to pass a point?

    b) What would the period of 'middle C' sound waves be?

4 If the following waves were travelling in opposite directions and met, they would interfere with each other. Match up the diagrams to show how.

1   **+**   **A** _____

2   **+**   **B**

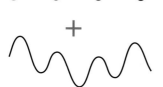

3   **+**   **C**

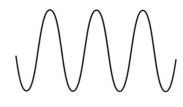

9 Periodic table

» Structure of the periodic table

Worked example

Explain why a balloon filled with helium floats in air, but a balloon filled with xenon sinks.

The density of the helium is lower than the density of air, whereas the density of xenon is greater than the density of air.

Know

1 State what is meant by each of the following terms:

   a) element

   b) periodic table

   c) a group in the periodic table

   d) a period in the periodic table

2 The noble gases are described as inert elements. State what is meant by 'inert'.

3 Give one use for each of the following noble gases. Choose a different use for each gas.

   a) helium

   b) neon

   c) argon

> **Hint**
>
> Do not confuse density with weight. You should not, for example, state that helium is lighter than air. One tonne of helium has the same weight as one tonne of air. However, it is correct to say that a given volume of helium is lighter than *the same volume* of air.

Apply

1 The table below gives some properties of the noble gases.

Name of noble gas	Boiling point (°C)	Density (g/dm³)
Helium	−269	0.18
Neon	−246	0.90
Argon	−186	1.78
Krypton	−152	
Xenon		5.9
Radon	−62	9.7

   a) Use the information in the table to state the relationship between:

      i) the boiling point and the position of the noble gas in the periodic table

      ii) the density and the position of the noble gas in the periodic table.

b) Use the information in the table to estimate a value for:

    i) the boiling point of xenon

    ii) the density of krypton.

c) Explain which balloon – one filled with xenon or one filled with radon – would fall to the ground the more quickly when released.

2 The diagram shows a part of the periodic table and the symbols for the first 20 elements.

H																	He

Li	Be											B	C	N	O	F	Ne
Na	Mg											Al	Si	P	S	Cl	Ar
K	Ca																

a) What name is given to a horizontal row of elements such as Li to Ne?

b) Give the names of two non-metals in the row Li to Ne.

c) Which is the least reactive element in the row Li to Ne.

» Group 1 (the alkali metals)

Worked example

State which alkali metal reacts most vigorously when heated in oxygen? Justify your answer.

Caesium reacts most vigorously. The reactivity of the alkali metals increases as you descend the group and caesium is at the bottom of the group.

Know

1 How does the reactivity of the alkali metals change as you go down the group?

2 Why do the alkali metals need to be stored in oil?

3 Name the gas produced when sodium reacts with water.

4 Name the compound formed when lithium reacts with oxygen.

Apply

1 When a small piece of lithium is added to water it fizzes and eventually disappears forming a solution.

a) Write a word equation for the reaction that takes place between lithium and water.

b) State and explain the effect that the solution formed has on litmus paper.

c) State two similarities and two differences between the reactions of lithium and potassium with water.

> **Hint**
> ....
> Remember how the reactivity of the alkali metals changes as you go down the group. Does the reactivity increase or decrease as you go down the group?

2 A small piece of lithium, potassium and caesium is added to water in three separate troughs. The table gives a description of the reaction of each metal.

Description of reaction	Metal
Burns with a lilac-coloured flame	
Explodes on contact with water	
Fizzes gently	

Copy and complete the table by giving the correct metal for each description.

3 This question is about the five group 1 metals; lithium (Li), sodium (Na), potassium (K), rubidium (Rb) and caesium (Cs).

Identity the substances A, B, C, D, E and F from the following descriptions.

a) Metal A has the lowest density of the five group 1 metals.

b) When the group 1 metal B is added to water it forms a small ball and moves around the surface of the water very quickly. A lilac flame is also seen. A gas C is given off. A white trail dissolves in the water to form a solution of compound D.

c) When the group 1 metal E is heated in oxygen it burns with a yellow-orange flame to form a white solid compound F.

» Group 7 (the halogens)

Worked example

There are five halogens in group 7 of the periodic table. These are fluorine, chlorine, bromine, iodine and astatine. All react with sodium when heated.

State which halogen reacts least vigorously when heated with sodium. Justify your answer.

Astatine reacts least vigorously with sodium. The reactivity of the halogens decreases as you go down the group. Astatine is the least reactive since it is at the bottom of the group 7.

>
>
> **Hint**
>
> Remember how the reactivity of the halogens changes as you go down the group. Does the reactivity increase or decrease as you go down the group?

Know

1 What is the meaning of the word 'halogen'?

2 How does the reactivity of the halogens change as you go down the group?

3 What is the name of the compound formed when sodium reacts with chlorine?

4 At room temperature bromine is:

A a brown gas

B a red-brown liquid

C a colourless gas

D a grey solid.

Apply

1 The table gives information about the first four elements in group 7 of the periodic table.

Element	Physical state at 20°C	Colour at 20°C	Name of compound formed when reacted with hydrogen
Fluorine	Gas	Pale yellow	Hydrogen fluoride
Chlorine	Gas	Pale green	Hydrogen chloride
Bromine	Liquid	Red-brown	Hydrogen bromide
Iodine	Solid	Dark grey	Hydrogen iodide

Astatine is the fifth element in Group 7. It is possible to make predictions about astatine by comparison with the other elements in Group 7.

a) Predict the physical state of astatine at 20°C.

b) Predict the colour of astatine at 20°C.

c) Predict the name of the compound formed when astatine reacts with hydrogen.

2 Chlorine reacts quickly with hot iron to form iron chloride. Bromine reacts less quickly with hot iron to form iron bromide.

Suggest how fluorine reacts with hot iron and name the compound formed.

3 These two hazards symbols are attached to a container of liquid bromine.

Suggest two safety precautions that a chemist should take when using bromine in an experiment. Justify your answers.

4 The table shows some information about the halogens in group 7 of the periodic table.

Halogen	Density (g/cm³)	Melting point (°C)	Boiling point (°C)	Atomic radius in pm
Fluorine	0.0017	−220	−188	72
Chlorine	0.0032	−101	−34	99
Bromine	3.1	−7		114
Iodine		114	184	133
Astatine	6.4	302	337	

a) Estimate a value for the boiling point of bromine.

b) Estimate a value for the density of iodine.

c) Estimate a value for the atomic radius of astatine.

d) State the relationship between the reactivity of the halogens and the atomic radius.

e) Explain why the densities of fluorine and chlorine are much lower than those of bromine, iodine and astatine.

10 Elements

» Representing elements and compounds

Worked example

What is the difference between a mixture of elements and a compound?

In a mixture the elements are not chemically bonded together and can be separated using appropriate physical processes (such as filtration, evaporation, distillation or chromatography).
In a compound the elements are chemically bonded together and can only be separated by chemical reactions.

Know

1 State what is meant by each of the following terms:

  a) element

  b) atom

  c) molecule

  d) compound

  e) polymer

Apply

1 State two ways in which a mixture of hydrogen and oxygen differs from water.

2 The box below shows the names of six pure substances.

| calcium | carbon | sodium chloride | mercury | nitrogen | ice |

Classify each of the substances in the box as either:

* a metallic element

* a non-metallic element

* a compound

> **Hint**
> Water has the chemical formula H_2O.

3 a) i) What do the following four substances have in common?

  * copper

  * sulfur

  * iron

  * tin

  ii) How does sulfur differ from the other three?

41

b) i) What do the following four oxides have in common?

- carbon dioxide

- manganese dioxide

- sulfur dioxide

- nitrogen dioxide

ii) How does manganese dioxide differ from the other three oxides?

4

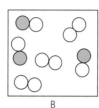
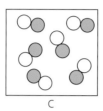
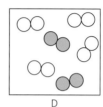

A   B   C   D

Which of the diagrams A, B, C and D represent:

a) a pure element

b) a pure compound

c) a mixture of two elements

d) a mixture of an element and a compound?

5 What can you deduce about the two substances E and F shown in the following diagrams?

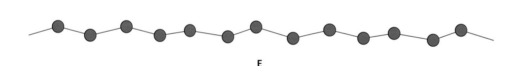

E

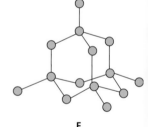

F

» Interpreting chemical formulae

Worked example

Give the names of the elements present in the compound with the formula $NaBrO_3$. How many of each type of atom are present?

The compound contains sodium, bromine and oxygen. There is one sodium atom, one bromine atom and three oxygen atoms.

Know

1 Give the chemical symbol for each of the following elements:

   a) lithium   **d)** fluorine

   b) beryllium   **e)** neon

   c) boron

2 Give the names of the elements that have the following symbols:

   a) Si   **d)** H

   b) P   **e)** He

   c) Ca

3 Give the chemical formula for each of the following elements:

   a) hydrogen   **d)** sulfur

   b) oxygen   **e)** fluorine

   c) chlorine

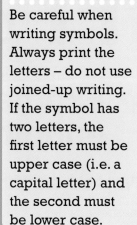

Hint

Be careful when writing symbols. Always print the letters – do not use joined-up writing. If the symbol has two letters, the first letter must be upper case (i.e. a capital letter) and the second must be lower case.

Apply

1 Give the names of the elements present in each the following compounds.

   a) KCl   **d)** $MgSO_4$

   b) Li_3N **e)** $Al(NO_3)_3$

   c) Na_2CO_3

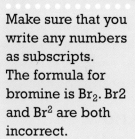

Hint

Make sure that you write any numbers as subscripts. The formula for bromine is Br_2. Br2 and Br^2 are both incorrect.

2 State how many of each type of atom are present in each of the following formulae:

   a) KCl   **d)** $MgSO_4$

   b) Li_3N **e)** $Al(NO_3)_3$

   c) Na_2CO_3

3 Give the name of each of the following compounds:

   a) KCl   **d)** $MgSO_4$

   b) Li_3N **e)** $Al(NO_3)_3$

   c) Na_2CO_3

4 Give the formula for each of the following compounds:

   a) carbon monoxide

   b) carbon dioxide

   c) sulfur trioxide

11 Chemical energy

» Exothermic and endothermic reactions

Worked example

Sherbet powder is a mixture of sodium hydrogencarbonate and tartaric acid.

When a student put some sherbet powder into his mouth he noticed that the mixture fizzed and also that his mouth became cold. Explain these two observations.

When sherbet powder mixes with water a reaction takes place.
The fizzing is caused by carbon dioxide gas being formed.
The reaction mixture gets cold because the reaction is endothermic; it
is taking in heat energy from the student's mouth.

Know

1 State what is meant by each of the following terms:

   a) exothermic reaction

   b) endothermic reaction

2 What happens to the temperature of a reaction mixture during an exothermic reaction?

Apply

1 The table shows the temperature changes that occur during four chemical reactions, A, B, C and D.

Reaction	Temperature at start (°C)	Temperature at end (°C)
A	20	42
B	22	5
C	21	10
D	23	31

   a) Calculate the temperature change for each reaction.

   b) State whether each reaction is exothermic or endothermic.

> **Hint**
>
> When asked to comment on two different observations, give your answer to each in a separate sentence. The fizzing is caused by a gas – you should give the name of this gas in your answer. If the student's mouth is getting cold then heat energy must be transferred from his mouth to the reaction mixture. What does this tell you about the reaction?

> **Hint**
>
> A temperature increase should have a + sign and a temperature decrease should have a − sign.

2 When sodium hydroxide solution is added to dilute hydrochloric acid a reaction takes place. Describe how you could find out if the reaction is exothermic or endothermic.

3 The following two graphs show how the temperature of a reaction mixture changes during the course of the reaction.

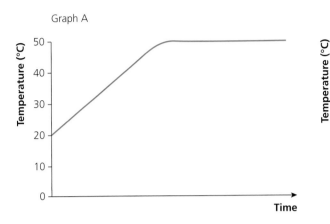

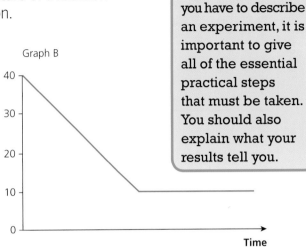

a) Does Graph A show an endothermic or an exothermic reaction? Justify your choice.

b) Does Graph B show an endothermic or an exothermic reaction? Justify your choice.

» Explaining energy changes

Worked example

When copper carbonate is heated it decomposes to form copper oxide and carbon dioxide. Fill in the gaps in the following sentences to explain why this reaction is endothermic.

More energy is taken in when the _____ in copper carbonate are broken than is given out when the bonds in _____ and _____ are formed.

More energy is taken in when the <u>bonds</u> in copper carbonate are broken than is given out when the bonds in <u>carbon dioxide</u> and <u>copper oxide</u> are formed.

Know

1 State what is meant by each of the following terms:

a) catalyst

b) chemical bond

2 Use words from the box to fill in the gaps in the sentences that follow.

endothermic	exothermic	given out	taken in

During a chemical reaction energy is _____ when chemical bonds are broken and energy is _____ when chemical bonds are made. If the energy given out is greater than the energy taken in, the reaction is _____. If the energy given out is less than the energy taken in, the reaction is _____.

Apply

1 Explain, in terms of bonds, why the reaction between magnesium and oxygen, to form magnesium oxide, is exothermic.

2 The following energy level diagram represents a reaction in which the energy of the reactants is the same as the energy of the products.

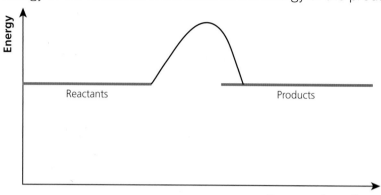

a) Draw an energy level diagram to represent an endothermic reaction. Draw an arrow on the diagram to show the overall energy change of the reaction.

b) Draw an energy level diagram to represent an exothermic reaction. Draw an arrow on the diagram to show the overall energy change of the reaction.

3 Copy the following energy level diagram for a reaction.

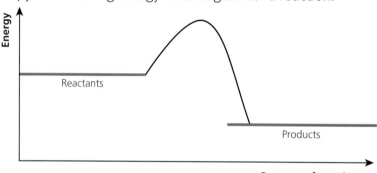

a) Draw an arrow on your diagram to show the energy taken in to the break the bonds of the reactants. Label this arrow A.

b) Draw a second arrow on your diagram to show the energy given out when the bonds of the products are made. Label this arrow B.

4 Copy the following energy level diagram for a reaction.

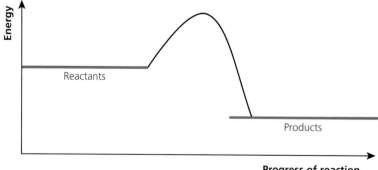

Draw a curve on your diagram to represent the effect of the catalyst on the reaction. Label the curve C.

12 Types of reaction

» Thermal decomposition

Worked example

A hydrated salt contains water that is chemically bonded to the salt. This water is known as 'water of crystallisation'. When a hydrated salt is heated it loses its water of crystallisation.

The equation for the action of heat on hydrated copper sulfate is:

$$CuSO_4.5H_2O(s) \rightarrow CuSO_4(s) + 5H_2O(g)$$

Explain why this reaction is classified as thermal decomposition.

The hydrated copper sulfate has been broken down into simpler substances by the action of heat.

Hint

You must not use the word 'decomposition' or 'decompose' in your answer. It is necessary to explain what is meant by decomposition.

Know

1 State what is meant by each of the following terms:

a) reactants

b) products

c) thermal decomposition

d) chemical reaction

e) physical change

2 Give the state symbol for each of the following physical states:

a) solid

b) liquid

c) gas

d) aqueous (dissolved in water)

3 What does the law of conservation of mass say about a chemical reaction?

Apply

1 a) You are supplied with two test tubes, a delivery tube bent at ninety degrees, a rubber bung and a beaker.

Draw a labelled diagram, including this apparatus, to show how you would heat a sample of hydrated cobalt chloride, collect the water vapour given off, and condense the vapour to liquid water.

Hint

The water vapour will need to be cooled to condense it.

b) What test would you do to show that the liquid collected is pure water?

c) How would you find out if the hydrated cobalt chloride gains mass, loses mass or stays the same mass on heating?

d) What change in mass would you expect? Explain your answer.

2 Blue crystals of hydrated copper sulfate are dry to the touch. However, when they are heated water vapour is given off.

The residue left after heating is a white powder. When water is added drop by drop to this white powder, the powder turns blue and gets quite hot.

A student wants to find what proportion of the crystals is water. He heats a weighed sample of hydrated copper sulfate in a crucible until all the water has been removed. He then allows the residue to cool and re-weighs it.

The table shows her results.

Mass of empty crucible	20.4 g
Mass of crucible + hydrated copper sulfate	32.9 g
Mass of crucible + white powder	28.9 g

a) Calculate the mass of hydrated copper sulfate used.

b) Calculate the mass of water given off.

c) Calculate the percentage of water present in the hydrated copper sulfate.

d) How could the student make sure that all of the water had been given off on heating?

e) Why does the white powder get hot when water is added to it?

» Combustion

Worked example

When magnesium is heated in air it burns with a bright, white flame, forming a white powder.

Explain why this reaction is classified as a combustion reaction, and write a word equation for the reaction.

The magnesium reacts with oxygen to release energy in the form of heat:

magnesium + oxygen → magnesium oxide

Know

1 State what is meant by the term combustion.

2 What is a fuel?

Apply

1 Classify each of the following reactions as combustion or thermal decomposition:

   a) Sodium burning in oxygen to form sodium oxide.

   b) Potassium hydrogencarbonate changing into potassium carbonate, water and carbon dioxide when heated.

   c) Methane burning in air to form carbon dioxide and water.

   d) Lead nitrate changing into lead oxide, nitrogen dioxide and oxygen when heated.

2 When magnesium burns in air, it reacts with oxygen to form magnesium oxide.

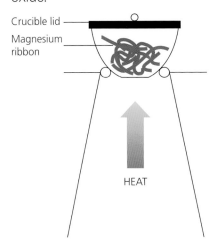

Crucible lid
Magnesium ribbon
HEAT

A student wants to find out the mass of magnesium oxide formed when a sample of magnesium burns in air. She uses the following method.

Step 1: Weigh a crucible and lid.

Step 2: Place some magnesium ribbon in the crucible, replace the lid and reweigh.

Step 3: Heat the crucible, as shown in the diagram, until the magnesium burns.

Step 4: Lift the lid from time to time until there is no sign of further reaction.

Step 5: Allow the crucible and lid to cool, and reweigh.

Step 6: Repeat the heating, cooling and reweighing until two consecutive masses are the same.

   a) i) Suggest why it is necessary to lift the lid from time to time (step 4).

      ii) Suggest why it is necessary to repeat the heating until two consecutive weights are the same (step 6).

b) The student records the following results:

Mass of empty crucible and lid	26.7 g
Mass of crucible, lid and magnesium	29.1 g
Mass of crucible, lid and magnesium oxide	30.7 g

  i) Calculate the mass of magnesium used in the experiment.

  ii) Calculate the mass of magnesium oxide formed in the experiment.

3 The diagram shows methane (natural gas) burning in air, and how the products of the reaction are collected and tested.

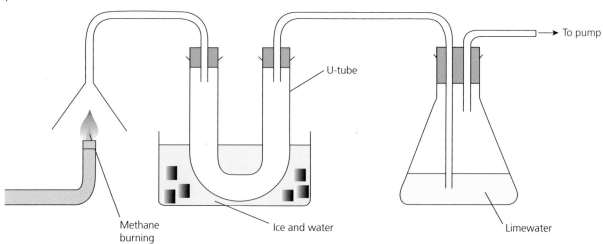

Methane burning

Ice and water

U-tube

Limewater

To pump

Water collects in the U-tube and the limewater truns milky, showing that carbon dioxide is formed. Suggest what two elements are present in methane.

13 Climate

» The carbon cycle

Worked example

Describe how burning wood from trees is affecting the carbon cycle.

Wood is a carbon-based fuel. When it burns carbon dioxide is formed and this goes into the atmosphere. Cutting down the trees to produce the wood for burning means that less carbon dioxide is taken out of the air by photosynthesis. The overall effect is that carbon dioxide is added to the atmosphere.

Hint

Consider the effects of both cutting down the trees to supply the wood, and the effect that burning the wood will have.

Know

1 The bar chart shows the percentage by volume of the gases in the Earth's atmosphere.

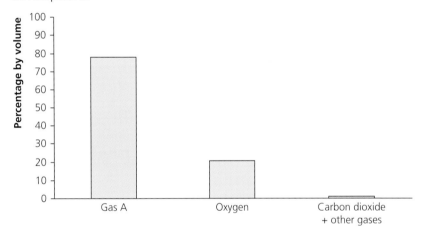

Give the name of gas A.

2 Which of the following gases occurs naturally in the Earth's atmosphere?

A argon

B carbon monoxide

C chlorine

D hydrogen

3 The gases in the Earth's earliest atmosphere were thought to come from which of the following?

A ice caps

B plants

C the ocean

D volcanoes

4 Explain what is meant by each of the following terms:

    a) fossil fuel

    b) carbon sink

Apply

1 Suggest how the growth of plants changed the percentage of oxygen and carbon dioxide in the Earth's early atmosphere.

2 One of the components of camping gas is propane. When propane burns in air the following reaction takes place:

$$\text{propane} + \text{oxygen} \rightarrow \text{carbon dioxide} + \text{water}$$

State how burning camping gas changes the amounts of gases in the atmosphere.

3 Apart from burning fossil fuels, describe two other activities that affect the amounts of gases in the atmosphere.

4 Describe how carbon dioxide in the atmosphere becomes calcium carbonate in rocks.

» The greenhouse effect and global warming

Worked example

Explain how global warming might affect the ice caps and how this may cause an increase in sea levels.

As the temperature of the Earth's surface rises, some of the thermal energy will be transferred to the ice caps. The rising temperature may cause more icebergs to form by weakening the glaciers, causing more cracks and making ice more likely to break off. As soon as the ice falls into the ocean, the ocean rises a little.

> **Hint**
>
> The melting of icebergs does not raise the sea level.

Know

1 Explain what is meant by each of the following terms:

    a) the greenhouse effect

    b) global warming

    c) weather

    d) climate

Apply

1 Explain how the greenhouse effect warms the Earth's atmosphere.

14 Earth resources

» Finite resources

Worked example

The worldwide demand for copper increased steadily from 2 million tonnes in 1900 to 20 million tonnes in 2010. The demand is predicted to continue to increase and could be as high as 40 million tonnes by 2030.

The deposits of copper in the Earth's crust are estimated to be about 289 million tonnes.

Even if all of the scrap copper is recycled, it would only meet 50% of the worldwide demand for copper.

Explain why there is some concern about the balance between supply and demand.

The demand for copper is rising, so copper deposits will eventually run out in the future. Therefore, supply will not meet the demand, even if all of the scrap copper is recycled.

Know

1 Explain what is meant by each of the following terms:

   a) natural resources

   b) extraction (of a metal)

   c) recycling

2 a) Give the name of the two most common elements found in the Earth's crust.

   b) Give the name of the most common metal found in the Earth's crust.

Apply

1 The table below shows some information about the extraction of copper from three different copper compounds obtained from the Earth's crust.

	Mass of compound (g)	Mass of copper extracted from the compound (g)	Mass of copper extracted per gram of compound (g)	Mass of copper extracted per kilogram of compound (g)
Compound 1	400	20	20/400 = 0.05	50
Compound 2	400	30	30/400 = 0.075	75
Compound 3	400	24		

   a) Calculate the mass of copper extracted per gram for compound 3.

   b) Calculate the mass of copper extracted per kilogram for compound 3.

c) Which compound produces the least waste material? Explain how you arrived at your answer.

d) Identify which of the following compounds might produce sulfur dioxide when copper is extracted from them:

- $CuCO_3$
- $CuFeS_2$
- CuS
- CuO
- Cu_2O
- Cu_2S

2 A mining company wants to find a new area to mine for metals.

A scientist from the mining company tests rocks from two possible sites. Her results are shown in the table.

Elements present in the rock	Percentage of each element present in the rock from site X	Percentage of each element present in the rock from site Y
Aluminium	14	14
Copper	7	0
Iron	9	11
Oxygen	39	45
Silicon	26	19
Other elements	5	

a) Calculate the percentage of other elements present in the rock from site Y.

b) State the similarities between the rocks found in each site.

c) Give two reasons why site X is the better site for the company to use to mine metals.

» Extracting metals using displacement reactions

Worked example

The order of reactivity of some metals is listed below. The list also contains the non-metal carbon. The most reactive metal is placed first.

sodium > calcium > magnesium > carbon > zinc > iron > lead > copper

Suggest how zinc could be obtained from zinc oxide.

Zinc oxide is mixed with carbon and the mixture is heated. The following reaction will take place:

zinc oxide + carbon → zinc + carbon dioxide

The metals sodium, calcium or magnesium would also convert zinc oxide to zinc, but these metals are more expensive than carbon.

> **Hint**
>
> Zinc can be obtained by making use of a displacement reaction. Choose a suitable substance that will be will displace zinc from zinc oxide, and will be the least expensive.

Know

1 Metals can be found in the Earth's crust as either minerals or ores. State what is meant, in this context, by the terms:

   a) mineral

   b) ore.

Apply

1 Suggest why gold is found uncombined in the Earth's crust, but aluminium is only found in compounds.

2 Copper could be obtained by heating copper oxide with either carbon or magnesium. The equations for the two reactions are:

$$CuO(s) + Mg(s) \rightarrow Cu(s) + MgO(s)$$

$$CuO(s) + C(s) \rightarrow Cu(s) + CO_2(g)$$

Suggest why, in industry, it is better to use carbon rather than magnesium to obtain copper from copper oxide.

> **Hint**
>
> Consider both the expense involved and also the ease with which the metal required can be separated from the mixture of products.

3 The reaction between aluminium and iron oxide is known as the thermite reaction. The diagram shows how the thermite reaction can be carried out.

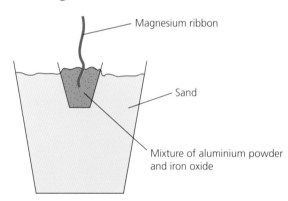

The magnesium ribbon is lit to ignite the reaction mixture. The reaction between aluminium and iron oxide is very exothermic. The word equation for the reaction is:

aluminium + iron oxide → aluminium oxide + iron

   a) What does the reaction suggest about the reactivity of aluminium compared with the reactivity of iron? Explain your answer.

   b) Explain which element is oxidised in this reaction.

   c) The thermite reaction can be used to join together two rails on a railway line.

   The reaction mixture is ignited and molten iron pours into the mould. The iron solidifies to create a join between the two rails. Explain why the iron produced in the reaction is molten.

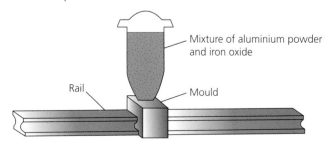

» Extracting metals using electrolysis

Worked example

Sodium is made by electrolysing sodium chloride. Write a word equation to represent this electrolysis.

sodium chloride → sodium + chlorine

Know

1 What is meant by the term electrolysis?

2 **a)** What is the name of the most common ore of aluminium?

   b) Give the name of the aluminium compound that is present in this ore.

Apply

1 The table gives some information about the temperature required to produce a metal by heating its oxide with carbon. It also gives the most cost-effective method of extraction.

Metal oxide	Minimum temperature to produce the metal by heating with carbon (°C)	Most cost-effective method of extraction of the metal
Aluminium oxide	2027	Electrolysis
Calcium oxide	2170	Electrolysis
Copper oxide	105	Heating with carbon
Iron oxide	747	Heating with carbon
lead oxide	350	Heating with carbon
Magnesium oxide	1625	Electrolysis
Zinc oxide	930	Heating with carbon

The order of reactivity of the metals listed in the above table is:

calcium > magnesium > aluminium > zinc > iron > lead > copper

Use the information in the table to explain how the method of extraction of a metal is related to its reactivity and the energy involved.

2 The table shows the results of electrolysing three molten metal halides (i.e. compounds of a metal and a halogen).

Molten compound	Observation at negative electrode	Substance formed at negative electrode	Observation at positive electrode	Substance formed at positive electrode
Sodium chloride	Flashes of light	Sodium	Pale green gas	Chlorine
Lead iodide	Shiny liquid ball		Purple gas	
Compound X	Shiny liquid ball		Orange–brown gas	

   a) Identify the elements formed at the negative and positive electrodes when lead iodide is electrolysed.

   b) Suggest a possible identity for compound X.

   c) Describe what you might expect to see at the negative and positive electrodes when molten potassium iodide is electrolysed.

15 Breathing

» What makes up an organism?

Worked example

The five senses are used to help us survive. When feeding, many animals use their senses to help them find food such as fruit.

Which of the five senses may be useful in finding fruit?

Smell – many fruits give off a pleasant smell to attract animals.

Sight – fruit is often brightly coloured, allowing animals to use their eyes to locate ripe fruit.

Taste – some fruit has a sweet taste to let the animal know that it is edible.

Touch – this will allow animals to pick the fruit and avoid spines.

Know

1 A person who weighs 75 kg has 49 kg of water in their body. Calculate the percentage of water that makes up this person.

2 The biceps muscle is made up of muscle cells, nerve cells, blood vessels and connective cells. Is the biceps muscle a cell, a tissue or an organ? Explain your answer.

3 Explain what each of the following does in the human heart:

a) muscle tissue

b) nervous tissue

4 Describe the function of each of the following systems:

a) breathing system

b) digestive system

c) reproductive system

d) nervous system

> **Hint**
>
> Here the percentage is simply a proportion of the whole mass, so 49 kg of the 75 kg mass, or 49/75 (and multiply by 100 to get a percentage value).

Apply

1 We have many other senses apart from sight, hearing, smell, taste and touch. Suggest names for the other senses that might be involved in the following examples:

a) dropping a pan because it is too hot

b) being able to ride a bicycle without falling off

c) knowing when it is lunchtime

d) wanting to drink some water

» The respiratory system

Worked example

Explain the difference between respiration and breathing.

Respiration is the chemical reaction that takes place in every cell, in which glucose is broken down to release energy.
Breathing is the movement of air into and out of our lungs.

Know

1 Fill in the missing words:

The respiratory system is made up of a tube that runs from the mouth called the _____. This is lined with tiny hairs called _____ and is protected by rings of _____.

The two bronchi split into many smaller tubes called _____. These end in small air sacs called _____.

2 What are the two structures labelled A and B on the diagram?

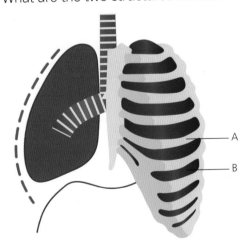

Apply

1 Name the rings labelled C on the diagram. Describe the function of these rings.

> **Hint**
>
> This is an important distinction. Although you may refer to the lungs as part of the respiratory system, try to keep the chemical process of respiration separate from the mechanical process of breathing or ventilation.

2 The substances in cigarette smoke paralyse and kill the ciliated cells of the trachea and bronchi. Explain how this could lead to:

a) a cough

b) increased chance of lung infections.

» Alveoli

Worked example

The composition of air was analysed before and after it entered a person's lungs. Less oxygen was found in the air leaving the lungs compared with air entering the lungs. Explain this observation.

Oxygen diffuses from the air entering the lungs into the blood capillaries through the alveoli. The oxygen is used by the body for respiration.

Know

1 Copy and complete the table below, showing the composition of air in inspired and expired air, using the word 'More' or 'Less'.

	Inspired air (%)	Expired air
Oxygen	20	Less
Carbon dioxide	0.04	

2 The alveoli are specially adapted so that gases can move into or out of the blood. Describe how each of the following adaptations helps gas movement:

a) large surface area

b) permeable

c) very thin walls

Apply

1 Copy and complete the following by filling in the missing words:

The carbon dioxide in the blood moves out into the _____ by a process called _____. This is the movement of molecules from an area of _____ concentration to an area of _____ concentration.

2 Describe how the following causes problems when a person smokes cigarettes:

a) nicotine

b) tar

3 A smoker develops a bad cough and starts to find that exercise becomes more difficult. Explain the reason for each of the following:

a) a smoker's cough

b) a smoker's reduced ability to exercise

4 Describe how asthma affects how a person breathes.

» The process of breathing

Worked example

The volume of the chest cavity increases when we breathe in. Explain how the follow bring about this change in volume:

a) intercostal muscles

b) diaphragm

a) Intercostal muscles contract and move the rib cage outwards and upwards, increasing the volume of the chest cavity.

b) The diaphragm contracts and flattens, making more room in the chest cavity for the lungs.

Know

1 Copy and complete the following by filling in the missing words:

The process of breathing in and out is known as _____. The movement of air into the lungs is called _____ and the movement of air out of the lungs is called _____.

2 Use the diagram to identify structures D, E and F.

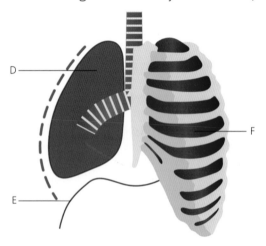

3 Put the following statements in the correct order for the events that occur when a person breathes in. (Numbers 1 and 5 have been done for you.)

1 intercostal muscles contract

ribs move inwards and downwards/ribcage moves upwards and outwards

diaphragm contracts/diaphragm relaxes

diaphragm becomes curved/diaphragm flattens

5 air moves into chest cavity

Apply

1 When we breathe in we use muscles to take air into the lungs. Breathing out does not normally require muscles to contract. Suggest why breathing out is normally a passive process.

2 When an athlete is competing in a race, their muscles are used to help them breathe out. Explain how this would help the athlete compete.

Hint

There are two sets of intercostal muscles – internal and external. Carry out some research to find out how these differ in their function.

16 Digestive system

» Diet

Worked example

Complete the following by filling in the missing words:

It is recommended that a person eats _____ portions of _____ or _____ each _____. The diet should be balanced and include mostly _____ with some _____ products, proteins such as _____ and a small amount of _____.

It is recommended that a person eats five portions of fruit or vegetables each day. The diet should be balanced and include mostly carbohydrates with some dairy products, proteins such as fish/meat and a small amount of fat.

Know

1 A person is worried about putting on too much weight. Suggest two pieces of advice that could help them lose weight.

2 Copy and complete the table on the right by filling in the type of drug.

3 Smoking has some serious effects on the body. Which component in cigarettes is responsible for each of the following:

   a) addiction to smoking cigarettes

   b) development of lung cancer as a result of smoking

Drug	Type
Ecstasy	Stimulant
Cannabis	
Cocaine	
Morphine	

Apply

1 Which of the following foods would an athlete eat to build up muscle for exercise:

   a) eggs

   b) meat

   c) pasta

   d) butter

   e) fish

2 Give an example of vigorous exercise.

3 In the UK laws exist that make it illegal to drink too much alcohol and drive a car. Explain why these laws exist.

> **Hint**
>
> Carry out some research to find out what the legal limits are. What is the legal age to drink alcohol? Do you think these limits are sensible?

» Food groups and a balanced diet

Worked example

Describe the benefits of a person eating the following foods as part of a balanced diet:
a) carbohydrates
b) proteins
c) lipids

a) Carbohydrates are a good source of energy and can be broken down to allow activities such as muscle contraction to take place.
b) Proteins are a source of the building blocks required for growth and repair of body tissues.
c) Lipids such as fats and oils are very high in energy. Small amounts of lipids are required for a healthy diet.

Know

1   Copy and complete the following by filling in the missing words:

   After visiting a doctor a person was told to cut down on saturated _____ in their diet. This could be done by reducing foods such as _____ and _____. Continuing to eat a large proportion of these foods could lead to an increase in _____ levels in the blood and possibly lead to the development of _____ disease.

2   Lipids are classified as either fats or oils.

   a) Describe the difference between fats and oils.

   b) Name one fat and one oil.

3   A balanced diet includes the correct amounts of different vitamins. Describe the function of the following vitamins:

   a) vitamin A

   b) vitamin C

   c) vitamin D

Apply

4   A young person's diet for a day is shown in the table.

   a) Which of components of the person's diet contain high levels of:

      i)   protein

      ii) carbohydrate

      iii) fat

   b) If the person wanted to change the meals to a vegetarian diet, what could they substitute for the foods high in protein?

Breakfast	Lunch	Dinner
Cereal	Salmon	Rice
Milk	Chips	Chicken
Buttered toast	Peas	Eggs
Tea	Water	Coffee

» The digestive system

Worked example

When eating food it is first taken into the mouth to start the process of digestion. Describe what the teeth and tongue do to the food in the mouth.

The food is crushed and broken down using the teeth and tongue. This breaks the food into smaller pieces, giving it a much larger surface area. This means that digestion takes place faster and the food can be swallowed easily.

Know

1 Saliva is secreted from glands in the mouth and helps with the process of digestion. Describe two functions of saliva in the mouth.

2 Using the key words in the box and your knowledge of enzymes, copy and complete the following.

| carbohydrates   increase   faster   pancreas   proteins |

Enzymes _____ the rate of reaction, allowing digestion of food to happen _____. In the mouth, saliva is mixed with the food and contains enzymes that start the breakdown of _____. The stomach produces another enzyme that breaks down _____. Many of the enzymes used in the small intestine are produced in the _____.

3 Look at the diagram below and name the structures labelled A, B, C and D.

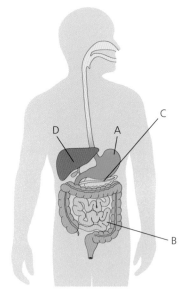

Apply

Short bowel syndrome (SBS) is a condition in which a lot of the small intestine is missing.

a) What is the main purpose of the small intestine?

b) How might the health of a person with SBS be affected by the condition?

c) Suggest how the diet of the person could be modified to help with the problems associated with SBS.

> **Hint**
> A question that asks you to 'suggest' an answer is usually very open-ended. Any sensible suggestion that answers the question will be accepted.

» The digestive process

Worked example

The complete digestion of our food requires both mechanical and chemical digestion. What is meant by:
a) mechanical digestion
b) chemical digestion?

a) Mechanical digestion is the breakdown of food using the teeth and tongue in the mouth. This breaks apart large pieces of food into smaller pieces.
b) Chemical digestion occurs in the mouth, stomach and small intestine, and involves the use of chemicals such as enzymes. Enzymes break down large food molecules into smaller molecules that can be absorbed into the blood.

Know

1 The drawing shows two types of teeth in the mouth.

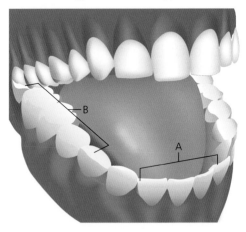

a) Identify the teeth labelled A and B.

b) Describe the function of:

i) A

ii) B

2 A person eats a cheese-and-ham pizza. Describe the roles of each of the following in the digestion of the pizza:

a) carbohydrase

b) protease

c) lipase

Apply

1 A student set up three test tubes to investigate the rate of reaction of the enzyme lipase. Lipase breaks down the fats in our food. The three test tubes contained the following:

- test tube 1: fat + lipase

- test tube 2: fat + lipase + bile

- test tube 3: fat + water

The table shows the results.

Test tube	Contents	Rate of reaction (g/min)
1	fat + lipase	3
2	fat + lipase + bile	24
3	fat + water	0

a) Explain why test tube 2 has a much faster rate of reaction that test tube 1.

b) Suggest what test tube 3 tells us about the enzyme lipase.

17 Respiration

» Staying alive

Worked example

Many bacteria can survive without oxygen, but almost every animal and plant alive needs it to survive. Why is oxygen essential for the survival of plants and animals?

Plants and animals use the oxygen for aerobic respiration. They combine it with sugars and this releases energy used for life processes such as movement.

Hint

When you give the answer 'respiration' to a question, always try to add the word 'aerobic' if the process is using up oxygen. Respiration without oxygen is known as anaerobic respiration.

Know

1 Water is vital for survival because it allows many substances to dissolve in it. Explain how the following are used for an animal's survival:

   a) dissolved oxygen

   b) dissolved minerals such as iron

2 Describe the ways in which a cactus reduces water loss in a desert.

Apply

1 In some areas of the world, people have to eat a diet that is made up of mainly carbohydrates and is very low in protein.

   a) What are proteins in the diet used for?

   b) Suggest an implication of eating a low-protein diet for long periods of time.

2 Water is essential for all living things and many animals have found ways of keeping water inside their bodies. Explain why urine is dark yellow when water is in short supply but pale yellow when plenty of water is available to drink.

3 When food supply is short, some animals hibernate. Explain how the following changes to a hibernating animal will help it survive periods of food shortage:

   a) reduced heart rate

   b) lower body temperature

   c) slower breathing rate

» Aerobic respiration

Worked example

Aerobic respiration involves the breakdown of glucose using oxygen. Describe where each of the following comes from:

a) oxygen

b) glucose

a) When we breathe, air moves into our lungs. The oxygen in the air diffuses into our blood and is taken to our cells for aerobic respiration.

b) A lot of the food we eat is digested and breaks down into glucose in our small intestine. The glucose is then absorbed into our blood and is transported to our cells for respiration.

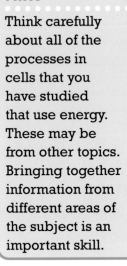

Hint

Think carefully about all of the processes in cells that you have studied that use energy. These may be from other topics. Bringing together information from different areas of the subject is an important skill.

Know

1 Copy and complete the equation for respiration shown:

$$glucose + oxygen \rightarrow \underline{\hspace{2cm}} \underline{\hspace{2cm}} + \underline{\hspace{2cm}}$$

2 Aerobic respiration releases energy from the glucose molecules. State three cell processes that rely on this release of energy.

Apply

1 A study was carried out in which the numbers of mitochondria in different types of cell were counted. The results are shown in the table:

Type of cell	Number of mitochondria
A	850
B	10
C	900

Cell type A was a muscle cell.

a) Suggest the type of cell for:

   i) cell B

   ii) cell C.

b) It was observed that the number of mitochondria in cell A increased after the person exercised for several months. Explain this observation.

» Anaerobic respiration in humans

Worked example

The cells in our bodies respire aerobically for most of the time. Sometimes, however, they respire anaerobically. Explain why a cell might respire anaerobically.

A cell may have to respire anaerobically instead of aerobically because it could be very active and using up the available oxygen very quickly. Also, in some situations the oxygen supply to the cell might be blocked, forcing cells to respire anaerobically for a short time.

Know

1 Write down the word equation for anaerobic respiration in animal cells.

2 Copy and complete the following by filing in the spaces with the correct word:

Anaerobic respiration means respiration without _____. It produces _____ _____ because _____ is not fully broken down into carbon dioxide and _____. The build-up of _____ _____ is toxic and so the body cells break it down as soon as _____ becomes available again.

3 The energy released by anaerobic and aerobic respiration was measured and recorded in a table:

Type of respiration	Energy released (kJ)
Aerobic	200
Anaerobic	10

a) What is meant by

i) aerobic respiration

ii) anaerobic respiration?

b) Calculate the energy released by anaerobic respiration as a proportion of the energy released by aerobic respiration.

c) Suggest why there is a difference between the energy released by the two processes.

Apply

1 An 800 m runner competes in a race. During the race his breathing rate increases.

a) Explain why the breathing rate increases during the race.

b) Explain why an athlete continues to breathe heavily even after the race has finished.

» Anaerobic respiration in microorganisms

Worked example

Anaerobic respiration can take place in animal cells and also in many microorganisms such as yeast. In yeast we call it fermentation.

Describe the differences between anaerobic respiration in animal cells and anaerobic respiration (fermentation) in yeast cells.

Anaerobic respiration in animal cells involves the production of lactic acid, whereas in yeast it produces the alcohol ethanol. Fermentation in yeast also produces the gas carbon dioxide.

Know

1 Copy and complete the word equation for anaerobic respiration in yeast cells:

$$glucose \rightarrow \text{_____} + \text{_____}$$

2 Describe two similarities between anaerobic respiration in animal cells and anaerobic respiration in yeast cells.

3 Name three types of microorganism.

4 Name three types of food that are produced by anaerobic respiration in microorganisms.

Apply

1 A student carried out an investigation to find out the best conditions needed for yeast to respire anaerobically. She set up five test tubes and recorded the number of bubbles produced by the yeast cells. The results are shown in the table.

Test tube	Yeast (cm³)	Glucose (cm³)	Temperature	Number of bubbles
1	5	5	10	5
2	5	5	20	43
3	5	5	50	12
4	5	0	20	0

a) What gas did the bubbles contain?

b) Explain the results for test tubes 1, 2 and 3.

c) What does test tube 4 tell us about yeast cells?

2 Explain what happens to bread when it is baked at high temperatures in an oven.

Hint

When presented with a table of data, read the stem of the question carefully. You may be asked to simply describe the trends in the data or, as in this case, to explain the results that were obtained.

18 Photosynthesis

» What do plants need to grow?

Worked example

Explain why a plant requires the following to survive:
a) carbon dioxide
b) oxygen
c) light

a) Plants require carbon dioxide for photosynthesis. They use the carbon dioxide to make sugars.
b) Plants need a supply of oxygen to carry out aerobic respiration. This provides the energy needed by the plants cells to stay alive.
c) Light is the 'driving force' for photosynthesis, allowing the plant to turn the carbon dioxide gas into sugars and other substances needed to survive.

Hint

Don't forget that all living things (which include plants) carry out the process of respiration. Apart from some bacteria, this is aerobic respiration, which means that almost all living things require oxygen to survive.

Know

1 A tree growing in a forest needs a supply of water to survive.

   a) Where does the water for the tree come from?

   b) How does the tree absorb the water it needs?

   c) What is the water used for?

2 Some very specialised plants are able to grow in hot deserts. What features of a desert mean that most plants are unable to survive?

Apply

1 A scientist called van Helmont grew a tree in a pot of soil for 5 years and measured:

   • the mass of the tree

   • the mass of the soil

   • the amount of water he gave it.

   The tree gained 75 kg but the soil lost just 0.05 kg. He concluded that the tree must be made from the water he had been giving it.

   a) Was he correct in saying this? Where else could the tree's mass have come from?

   b) Suggest why the soil lost 0.05 kg.

» The process of photosynthesis

Worked example

Photosynthesis produces glucose molecules that can be used for different functions in a growing plant. Describe three of the functions that glucose can be used for.

Glucose can be used for:
• respiration, where it is combined with oxygen to release the energy that keeps plant cells alive
• the production of cellulose, which is used to make the cell walls of new plant cells
• the production of starch, which is an insoluble storage molecule, allowing the glucose to be used later as the plant grows.

Know

1 Copy and complete the paragraph by filling in the missing words:

   Plants carry out photosynthesis by using energy from the _____ to combine _____ _____ with water to make _____ and glucose. The _____ of the plant absorb the water while the _____ absorb the _____ _____.

2 What is meant by a limiting factor?

Apply

1 Without plants, life would be very different. They are essential for organisms to survive on Earth. Give examples of how plants contribute to the following:

   a) allowing living things to respire

   b) production of food

   c) production of medicines

   d) production of materials for clothing

2 A student did an investigation in which he measured the rate of photosynthesis in a plant kept under different conditions. The results are shown in the table.

Plant	Temperature (°C)	Carbon dioxide concentration (%)	Rate of photosynthesis
A	20	1	100
B	20	2	100
C	25	1	120
D	25	2	120

   a) What is the limiting factor in the investigation? Explain your answer.

   b) Suggest how this factor could limit the rate of photosynthesis.

   c) Apart from carbon dioxide and temperature, name another factor that might be important in controlling the rate of photosynthesis in this plant.

» Leaf structure

Worked example

Describe the functions of each of the following leaf components:

a) palisade layer

b) spongy layer

c) waxy cuticle

a) The palisade layer of the leaf is made up of cells that are packed full of chloroplasts. These carry out photosynthesis.

b) The spongy layer has cells with air spaces between them. These air spaces allow gases to be exchanged and water to evaporate. The cells also contain chloroplasts and help with photosynthesis.

c) The cuticle is a waxy layer that prevents water from evaporating from the outer leaf cells. This prevents the leaf from drying out.

Know

1 On a copy of the diagram, add a label to the plant cell to show where photosynthesis takes place.

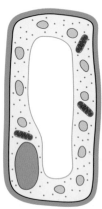

2 Describe how each of the following helps a leaf carry out its function:

a) large surface area

b) very thin

c) has a network of veins

3 On a copy of the diagram, add labels to show the following:

a) waxy cuticle

b) spongy layer

c) air spaces

d) palisade layer

e) stomata

Apply

1 A student measured the leaf area of three leaves from three different types of plant. She recorded them in a table:

Plant	Leaf 1 area (cm^2)	Leaf 2 area (cm^2)	Leaf 3 area (cm^2)	Average leaf area (cm^2)
A	40	41	39	40
B	3	1	2	2
C	15	15	12	14

a) Which leaf would be best for absorbing as much sunlight as possible?

b) Which leaf comes from a plant growing in a hot, dry environment?

c) Suggest one other feature of the leaves that the student could have measured.

» Root structure

Worked example

Scientists used a very fine syringe to take a sample of liquid from the stem of a plant. A second sample was taken from a different position on the stem and the liquids were analysed.

- Sample A contained mainly water with some minerals.
- Sample B contained water with sugar dissolved in it.

Which sample was taken from the xylem vessels and which was taken from the phloem? Explain your answer.

Sample A was taken from the xylem as this transports water and minerals from the soil up to the leaves of the plant.
Sample B was taken from the phloem as this transports the sugars made by photosynthesis to the rest of the plant.

Know

1 Explain how the roots of a plant can help with the following:

a) preventing the plant from blowing over in strong winds

b) allowing the plant to photosynthesise

2 Xylem vessels and phloem tissue are both used for transport in a plant.

a) How is the xylem adapted for its function?

b) Describe two ways in which xylem and phloem differ in their structure and function.

> **Hint**
>
> Although the roots of most plants are not exposed to light and are not directly involved in photosynthesis, they do contribute an important component. Write the equation for photosynthesis and think about where the materials come from.

3 Use the diagram to explain the role of the root hair cells and describe how they are adapted for their function.

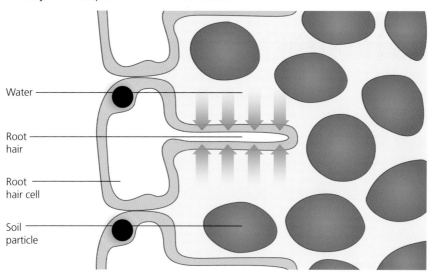

Water

Root hair

Root hair cell

Soil particle

Apply

1 A new fertiliser is being marketed that promises to allow gardeners to grow better plants. Two of the key ingredients are:

- magnesium sulfate

- ammonium nitrate

Explain how each of these ingredients could help to improve the growth of the gardener's plants.

19 Evolution

» Adaptations

Worked example

Polar bears live in the Arctic and are well adapted to survival in cold environments.

Describe some of the adaptations shown by a polar bear and say how they help it survive.

Polar bears are adapted to a cold environment in many ways including;
- *Thick fur – this traps a layer of insulating air, keeping the polar bear warm even on the coldest days.*
- *Small ears – being small means that heat loss is reduced.*
- *A thick layer of fat under the skin – this acts as an insulating layer, preventing too much heat loss from the blood.*

Hint

You may be asked about the adaptations of animals and plants that you have not encountered before. If a photograph or illustration is provided, look carefully at the organism and try to think about the adaptations needed for the place it lives.

Know

1 Why do different organisms show different adaptations?

2 Cacti grow in hot, dry deserts. Explain how each of the following adaptations helps cacti to survive:

   a) thick, waxy cuticle

   b) fleshy stem

   c) leaves reduced to spines

   d) tap roots extending deep into the soil

Apply

1 Cattle have a layer of hair and they live in a wide range of habitats all over the world. The depth of the hair coat of one type of cattle was measured every two months for a year. The results were recorded in a table:

Month	Depth of coat (mm)
Jan	4.6
Mar	2.7
May	2.1
Jul	1.8
Sep	2.6
Nov	3.7

   a) Explain the trend seen in coat depth.

   b) Suggest how the coat depth of the cattle can change over time.

» The theory of evolution by natural selection

Worked example

The last universal common ancestor was likely to have been a single-celled organism that existed on Earth some 3.5 billion years ago.

Why is it called the last universal common ancestor?

The single-celled organism is the life form from which all other life on Earth developed. It is the point at which life began to change into the different species that we see around us today.

Know

1 Using the key words in the box, copy and complete the following.

| species   DNA   biodiversity   population |

Variation is the difference between individuals due to their _____. The difference between individuals within a _____ is known as _____. It can also mean the different types of _____ found in different habitats.

2 A scientist has stated that 'evolution cannot take place if there is no variation'. Explain why evolution requires variation.

Apply

1 The following statements describe the stages that occur during the process of evolution. Put these statements into the correct order:

- The advantageous characteristics are passed on to the next generation.

- Some individuals are better adapted than others.

- Individuals within a population show variation.

- These are therefore more likely to reproduce.

- These individuals are more likely to survive to a mature age.

2 Around 66 million years ago the dinosaurs became extinct. Use your knowledge of the theory of evolution to explain how a species could become extinct.

» Charles Darwin

Worked example

In 1859 Charles Darwin published his theory of evolution. Describe Darwin's theory of evolution.

Darwin said that all organisms show variation. There may be competition between the organisms and so some may have an advantage. These ones are most likely to survive and most likely to reproduce. The favourable characteristics of the survivors will be passed on to the next generation. Over a long period of time this will cause a change in the organism.

Know

1 Explain what Charles Darwin meant by the term 'natural selection'.

2 Darwin travelled to the Galapagos Islands aboard the survey ship the *Beagle*.

   a) What did Darwin notice on the voyage of the *Beagle* that helped him develop his theory when he returned back to England?

   b) What made the Galapagos Islands an ideal place for Darwin to make observations supporting the theory of evolution?

Apply

1 In 1864 Herbert Spencer first used the term 'survival of the fittest' to describe the natural selection that Darwin described in his book.

   a) What is meant by 'survival of the fittest'?

   b) Suggest why 'survival of the fittest' is not always an accurate description of the process of evolution.

2 The drawing shows some of the birds that Darwin sent back from his visit to the Galapagos Islands.

> **Hint**
>
> Think carefully about what we mean by being the 'fittest'. It often means being the biggest, strongest or most healthy. Sometimes, however, other features (such as small size) may be an advantage.

It is thought that the birds all had a common ancestor with a single beak shape. Suggest how the birds could have developed into the variety of beak shapes seen.

» Biodiversity

Worked example

It is important that we try to protect and maintain the biodiversity in the world around us.

a) Give two reasons why maintaining biodiversity is a benefit.

b) Give examples of the ways in which humans have tried to maintain biodiversity.

a) Maintaining biodiversity is important because:
   • species are less likely to become extinct in a diverse habitat
   • many species may be of potential benefit to us, such as in the production of new medicines.

b) We have tried to preserve biodiversity by setting up national parks, conservation zones and introducing laws to protect the environment.

Know

1 Give examples of each of the following types of biodiversity:

   a) biodiversity within a species

   b) biodiversity between species

   c) biodiversity between habitats

Apply

1 The numbers of different species of mammal found in three different habitats in Argentina were measured and the results recorded in a table:

Habitat	Number of mammal species
Mountain	45
Forest	100
Grassland	120

   a) Suggest how the number of species in a habitat could be measured.

   b) Explain which habitat has the greatest biodiversity.

   c) Suggest why this study may not give a true value for the biodiversity of each habitat.

> **Hint**
>
> Biodiversity can mean simply the number of different species, but it may also depend on the number of individuals of each of the species. A habitat could have many species, but if one species makes up 99% of the organisms, the habitat will have low biodiversity.

20 Inheritance

≫ Predators and their prey

Worked example

The drawing shows a cheetah hunting.

Describe how the cheetah is adapted as a predator.

Cheetahs have several adaptions that help them hunt for prey. These include:
- powerful leg muscles that allow them to chase and catch their prey as it tries to escape
- sharp teeth and claws to hold onto their prey and kill it once it is caught
- good eyesight to spot the prey and judge its distance when hunting
- camouflaged fur that helps them blend in with the background so that they can approach as close to their prey as possible.

Know

1 Explain how each of the following helps to protect the animal from predators:

   a) Rabbits have powerful muscles in their back legs.

   b) The monarch butterfly stores toxins from the plants it eats in its body.

   c) Leaf insects have flattened bodies that resemble the leaves on which they feed.

2 The photograph shows insects called shield bugs forming a tight group on a leaf.

Suggest how this behaviour could help individuals survive an attack by a predator.

Apply

1 The monarch butterfly stores toxins in its body and is brightly coloured. The viceroy butterfly looks almost identical to the monarch but does not have toxins in its body. Suggest how the viceroy benefits from looking the same as the monarch butterfly.

2 The drawing represents the skulls of two animals viewed from above.

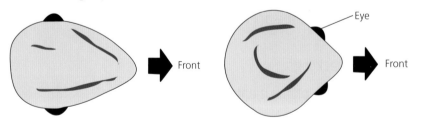

Which animal represents a predator and which represents the prey? Explain your answer.

Hint
The viceroy butterfly is an example of a mimic. Try researching to find out other examples of mimics. How do they benefit from this type of lifestyle?

» From the genome to DNA

Worked example

Which two of the following cells from a person are genetically identical?
- egg cell
- liver cell
- red blood cell
- skin cell

The cells that contain identical genetic material are the liver cell and the skin cell.
The egg cell is haploid – having one copy of the genome instead of two.
The red blood cell has lost all of its genetic material to make more room to carry oxygen.

Know

1 The diagram shows a short section of a DNA molecule:

   a) What is the name given to the shape of this molecule?

   b) Who were the scientists who were awarded a Nobel prize for discovering its structure?

   c) What contribution did Rosalind Franklin make to the discovery of DNA?

2 Explain how a molecule as long as DNA can fit into the nucleus of a living cell.

Apply

1 The diagram shows all of the chromosomes from the nucleus of a cell.

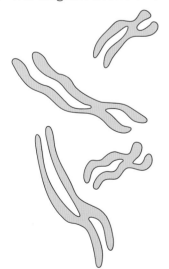

   a) Is this a diploid or haploid cell? Explain your answer.

   b) How many molecules of DNA are shown in the diagram? Explain your answer.

2 Copy and complete the base pairs for the section of DNA shown.

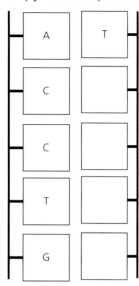

» Monohybrid inheritance

Worked example

Complete the following by filling in the missing words:

A section of DNA that gives us a particular characteristic is called a _____. We have two copies of each, known as _____, one from our _____ and one from our _____. Cells with two copies are known as _____ and include most of our body cells. Cells with just one copy are called _____ and include the egg and _____ cells.

A section of DNA that gives us a particular characteristic is called a gene. We have two copies of each, known as alleles, one from our mother and one from our father. Cells with two copies are known as diploid and include most of our body cells. Cells with just one copy are called haploid and include the egg and sperm cells.

Know

1 Copy and complete the table by adding either the characteristic or phenotypes.

Characteristic	Phenotypes
Eye colour	
Blood group	A, B, AB, O
Hair colour	
Earlobe shape	
	Purple pea flowers; white pea flowers

2 A plant with red berries was crossed with a plant with yellow berries. All of the new plants had red berries. Work out the following:

   a) the dominant allele

   b) the recessive allele

   c) the phenotype of the new plants

   d) the genotype of the new plants.

Apply

1 A male, XY, and a female, XX, have a baby. Copy and complete the Punnett square to show the chance of the baby being either male or female.

> **Hint**
>
> Remember that humans have 23 pairs of chromosomes, with 22 pairs looking the same. One pair can be different: X and X in females; X and Y in males.

» Mutations and their effects

Worked example

Mutations can occur in normal body cells as well as in the sex cells, eggs or sperm. Suggest why a mutation in a body cell is unlikely to lead to an evolutionary change in that species.

A mutation in a body cell will only affect the individual organism. The effects may be serious for that individual, but the mutation will not be passed on to future generations.
A mutation in a sex cell has a chance of being passed on to the next generation. Any effect will be inherited and will affect all future generations. Depending on the mutation, this may have an effect on the evolution of that species.

Know

1 Antibiotics are used to treat some infections by killing bacteria. Bacteria may show mutations that make them resistant to the antibiotics.

   a) What is meant by a mutation?

   b) Explain how the mutation could be an evolutionary advantage to the bacteria.

   c) Suggest why the over-use of antibiotics is not encouraged.

2 Distinguish between the following pairs of terms:

a) mutagen and carcinogen

b) malignant tumours and benign tumours

c) genetic disorders and communicable diseases

Apply

1 Cystic fibrosis is a genetic disease in which a large amount of sticky mucus is produced. Explain the consequences of excessive mucus production in the following parts of the body:

a) lungs

b) reproductive system

c) digestive system

2 Sickle-cell anaemia is a genetic condition in which some of the blood cells change shape and are destroyed by the body.

A male and female carrier of sickle-cell anaemia plan to have a baby. Copy and complete the Punnett square below to explain the chances of the baby suffering from the condition.

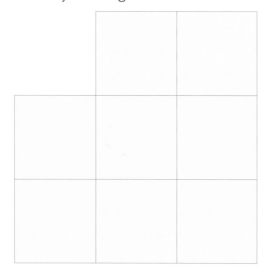

Index